Wavelength			Frequency	Wave Number	Energy	
cm.	mμ	μ	Mc./sec.	cm.$^{-1}$	kcal./mol	
10^{-8}						X-RAYS 0·5–10Å
10^{-7}	1					
10^{-6}	10					FAR AND EXTREME ULTRAVIOLET 1–185mμ
10^{-5}	10^2			10^5	300	
						ULTRAVIOLET 185–400 mμ
10^{-4}	10^3	1		10^4	30	VISIBLE 400–1,000 mμ
						NEAR INFRARED 10,000–4,000 cm.$^{-1}$
10^{-3}	10^4	10		10^3	3	INFRARED 4,000–400 cm.$^{-1}$
10^{-2}	10^5	10^2		10^2	0·3	FAR INFRARED 400–10 cm.$^{-1}$
10^{-1}			3×10^5	10	0·03	
1			3×10^4	1	0·003	MICROWAVE 1 mm.–10 cm.
10			3×10^3	10^{-1}		
10^2			3×10^2			RADIOFREQUENCY < 3,000 Mc./sec.
10^3			30			

The Electromagnetic Spectrum

ADVANCED PRACTICAL
INORGANIC CHEMISTRY

Advanced
Practical
Inorganic
Chemistry

D. M. ADAMS and **J. B. RAYNOR**

Department of Chemistry
University of Leicester, England

John Wiley & Sons, Ltd.   London · New York · Sydney

Set by Santype Ltd., of Salisbury
and printed in Great Britain by
Barnicotts Ltd. of Taunton.

To

MARION and ROSEMARY

Preface

For many years practical inorganic chemistry has been virtually synonymous with qualitative and quantitative analysis. With the growth of modern inorganic chemistry, most universities and colleges teaching advanced aspects of the subject have modified their courses to include a wide range of the preparative and structural techniques which are the practical basis of the new growth. It is a reflection upon the stage of development that these new emphases in teaching have reached that there does not exist – to our knowledge – a textbook of practical inorganic chemistry presenting a modern approach at honours degree level.

In this book we present a collection of ideas and tested experiments suitable for use up to honours degree level. We have not included any general account of volumetric or gravimetric methods or of qualitative analysis as there are many excellent accounts available. Furthermore, the place of a detailed selection of these methods in an honours degree course is debatable. We prefer to see the student analyse compounds of his own making rather than an 'unknown': the significance of accuracy, purity and stoicheiometry then becomes readily apparent.

The order in which other teachers will wish to present this material may well differ from our own and for this reason we have not laid out the book to our own teaching plan. We feel, however, that Section I should be covered in the first two years. Section II is third year work and is probably best covered in a short, fairly intensive course, rather than in a few hours a week over many weeks. This is because most of the experiments are more than one day's work and will suffer if left at an intermediate stage for a week.

A few remarks are necessary about the cost and organization of the advanced course in Section II. We have assumed availability of certain major pieces of equipment, mainly spectrometers; a certain amount of non-standard glassware is also employed. The annual cost of the course is not great. With the exception of the platinum metals and a few other elements (e.g. rhenium), we have not allowed cost of chemicals to preclude an experiment. This is not as extravagant as it may sound because relatively few of the class will do any one experiment if the whole range of experiments described in Section II is run concurrently.

Throughout the courses contained in this book we rely heavily upon the students' initiative. Although there is obviously a great deal of fact and technique to be taught through these experiments, there are also many points from which they can be extended and developed. The frequent questions are an attempt to foster this process.

Throughout this book, we have drawn freely from *Inorganic Syntheses* and from the purely preparative material contained in W. G. Palmer's *Experimental Inorganic Chemistry* and H. F. Walton's *Inorganic Preparations*, in many cases making some alterations. We have done this in order to make the book complete in itself and also because these books are probably more readily available for further consultation than (say) *J. prakt. Chem.* and other original sources, which we have also consulted.

In formulating our ideas on the teaching of practical inorganic chemistry, we have benefited greatly from discussion and correspondence with colleagues in several Departments of Chemistry, in particular those at Nottingham University. We are greatly indebted to Dr. R. D. W. Kemmitt who was co-designer of the course from which Section II developed, and who has made many valuable comments and suggestions during the preparation of this book. Finally, we would like to acknowledge the help of many undergraduate students of this Department in testing and developing these experiments.

D. M. ADAMS

J. B. RAYNOR

Contents

APPENDICES

Section I

Structural, Analytical and Preparative Studies

Chapter 1

Solid State Chemistry

Solid state chemistry is an important part of a balanced study of inorganic chemistry; indeed much of inorganic chemistry is the chemistry of the solid state. Early in his studies the student should become familiar with the essential details of the commoner types of structure so that they may form a framework upon which many of the more advanced aspects of structural inorganic chemistry may be built. Little difficulty should then be experienced in understanding the structural aspects even of such complex systems as the non-stoicheiometric oxides, sulphides, hydrides, etc., which are the object of much current research.

Two major difficulties seem to attend the presentation and understanding of solid state structural inorganic chemistry. Firstly, there is a great body of fact to be considered, much of which is apparently unrelated: in some ways the situation parallels the schoolboy's view of inorganic chemistry as a whole! Secondly, there is the inherent problem of visualizing often complex three-dimensional structures. This chapter offers suggestions for experiments which not only aim to dispel much of the problem of visualization, but also try to emphasize certain structural and geometrical relationships. They are meant to *illustrate* lectures on structural inorganic chemistry and do not in themselves provide sufficient instruction in the topics considered.

Classification of solid state structures

A brief discussion of the methods of classification of solid state structures is essential if the full purpose of the following experiments is to be appreciated. As it is not the purpose of this book to deal with theory which is readily available elsewhere, only a very brief introduction is given. The student is urged to consult the general references listed at the end of this section.

3

The method of classification used is effectively that of A. F. Wells.[1-3] Instead of attempting to classify crystals as ionic, covalent, etc., we rely simply upon topological relationships. To develop such a system of classification we focus attention first of all upon purely geometrical considerations. For example, given two different types of atom, A and B, what arrangements of A and B in space are geometrically possible? We can ask this question for each value of n for compositions AB_n. Note that we have *not* asked 'what structural types of stoicheiometry AB_n are known?'. We have asked a perfectly general topological question; the results of our investigations may now be compared with what is *in fact* known about the crystal structures of compounds AB, AB_2, ... Questions of this sort are really extensions of the general question regarding the possible arrangements of similar points in space, which is answered by a description of the 230 crystallographic space groups. This approach enables us to relate geometrically many apparently unrelated compounds (e.g., K_2SiF_6, $RbCaF_3$ and $Cs_3Tl_2Cl_9$; or NaCl, CaF_2 and diamond), to appreciate more readily the structural relationships between various 'types', and to reduce the burden on the memory.

A variety of more specific questions may profitably be asked. For example, we might enquire whether it is possible to interconnect points in space in such a manner that the disposition of bonds about each point is tetrahedral, and whether there be more than one way of doing this. Put more specifically, is the diamond structure the only *possible* one for the linking of tetrahedrally hybridized atoms?

With many complex structures it is often profitable to focus attention on *coordination polyhedra* rather than on (say) layers of close-packed ions with some of the interstices filled. This approach lends itself well to the creation of systems of classification and greatly assists the visualization of complex structures. Perhaps the best known example of the use of this device is in the description of the mineral silicates. Although they may correctly be described as close-packed layers of oxygen atoms with silicon in tetrahedral holes and various cations in octahedral interstices, they are much more readily understood if discussed in terms of a basic SiO_4 tetrahedral unit. Some experiments below give an introduction to the use of polyhedra in solid state studies. In all the experiments below, there is room for variation. It is hoped that the student will allow his interest to lead him to extend and develop experiments and to devise new ones.

General references

1. A. F. Wells, *Structural Inorganic Chemistry*, 3rd edition, Oxford, 1962.
2. A. F. Wells, *The Third Dimension in Chemistry*, Oxford, 1956.
3. A. F. Wells, *Solid State Physics*, Academic Press Inc., New York, 1958, Vol. 7, p. 425.
4. J. S. Anderson, *Proc. Chem. Soc.*, 1964, 166.

Equipment

For experiments requiring balls of various sizes, the cheapest material is expanded polystyrene. Spheres of several sizes are available.* They can be painted and stuck together in layers or other units and are so cheap that they can reasonably be regarded as expendables. Lids from filter paper boxes are suitable as bases for containing structures which are not stuck together. For demonstrations and experiments concerned with close-packing, it is recommended that sheets of close-packed spheres stuck together be prepared ready for use. An alternative type of model for this purpose is the ball-and-rod type shown in figure 33 of general reference 1.

In some cases, it is useful to have available sets of ball-and-spring models for comparison with structures built from spheres. Most of the commercial sets are suitable. Crystal structures built from balls and rods can also be purchased.†

Polyhedra in expanded polystyrene are conveniently joined by short lengths of cocktail stick or, for more permanent models, with an impact adhesive.‡

> NOTES (i) These experiments are best performed in the sequence given, as they form a logical progression.
>
> (ii) They are meant to *illustrate* lectures on structural inorganic chemistry and do not in themselves provide sufficient instruction in the topics considered.
>
> (iii) A copy of general reference 1 is essential for the completion of most of these experiments.

1.1 Close-Packing of Like Spheres

(i) Using the prepared sheets of close-packed spheres,§ stack them so as to give (a) cubic close-packing, ABC, ABC, ABC ..., (b) hexagonal close-packing, AB, AB, AB .... Are there any other ways of

---

* From Elford Plastics Limited, Wood Street, Elland, Yorkshire.
† From Crystal Structures Ltd., 339, Cherry Hinton Road, Cambridge.
‡ Enquiries concerning these polyhedra should be addressed to Crystal Structures Ltd.
§ Sheets of 24 one-inch-diameter polystyrene spheres are recommended.

stacking close-packed layers? Is it possible to make a structure with a repeat unit ABAC?

(ii) Make models of c.c.p. and h.c.p. structures using free spheres, or the ball-and-rod type of reference 1, figure 33. Identify the unit cell of each; replace all the spheres of one unit cell by coloured spheres. Write down the symmetry elements possessed by each unit cell. What classes of solid can be represented by close-packed models?

(iii) In both h.c.p. and c.c.p. structures identify (a) tetrahedral sites and (b) octahedral sites. Make models of each type of 'site' using coloured spheres and build these into your models of h.c.p. and c.c.p. structures. What is the ratio of tetrahedral to octahedral sites?

(iv) Identify the positions of (a) tetrahedral and (b) octahedral sites in models of the unit cells of h.c.p. and c.c.p. structures.

References

1. A. F. Wells, *Structural Inorganic Chemistry*, 3rd edition, Oxford, 1962.
2. W. E. Addison, *Structural Principles in Inorganic Compounds*, Longmans, London, 1961.

1.2 Filling of Tetrahedral and Octahedral Sites

Use prepared sheets of close-packed spheres (see previous experiment) stacked to give (a) c.c.p. and (b) h.c.p.

1. Tetrahedral sites

(i) Using very small spheres* fill *all* the tetrahedral sites in both c.c.p. and h.c.p. structures. Draw diagrams of the unit cell of each structure so formed. Suggest why no compound is known in which all tetrahedral sites in a h.c.p. host lattice are filled. Can all the tetrahedral sites in an ... ABAC ... close-packed structure be filled? Compare your models with the structure of CaF_2.

(ii) Develop a formula for the density of a c.c.p. structure in which all the tetrahedral sites are filled. Consider both cases, $r_1/r_2 \leqslant 0 \cdot 225$ and $> 0 \cdot 225$.

(iii) Fill one half of the tetrahedral sites in both h.c.p. and c.c.p. lattices. Draw diagrams of the unit cell of each structure. Repeat, filling only one quarter of the sites. What are the coordination numbers of the host atoms and the interstitial atoms in all these

* Glass beads 6 mm. in diameter are suitable.

structures? Compare your models with the structures of Wurtzite, zinc blende and SiS_2.

2. Octahedral sites

(i) Using small spheres* fill all the octahedral sites in both c.c.p. and h.c.p. structures. Work out a formula for the density of the structure based on h.c.p. for $r_1/r_2 \leqslant 0.414$.

(ii) For both c.c.p. and h.c.p. structures fill (a) one half and (b) one third of the octahedral sites in such a way as to form 'layer' structures, i.e., alternate layers of sites are filled. Draw diagrams of the unit cells of these structures and record the coordination numbers of both host and interstitial atoms. Compare your models with the known layer structures of $CrCl_3$, BiI_3 and the cadmium halides.

Is it possible to form a close-packed layer structure of stoicheiometry A_2B_3, where B is the host lattice?

1.3 Close-Packing of Equal Spheres of Two Kinds: Complex Oxides and Halides

Close-packed structures can be formed from atoms of two kinds provided their sizes are comparable. For this experiment use spheres of equal size and of two different colours.

(i) Make as many different close-packed layers as possible of stoicheiometry AB_2. Then stack the various layers in different sequences and draw diagrams of the coordination spheres of both A- and B-type atoms. Is there any form of structure of this sort in which A atoms are not adjacent?

(ii) Repeat the above for stoicheiometry AB_3. These systems form a basis for the description of the structures of complex oxides and halides, $A_nB_mX_{3n}$. Close-packed layers of composition AX_3 act as host lattice to smaller B cations which fit into octahedral interstices.

What fraction of octahedral sites must be filled to give the following types: ABX_3, $A_3B_2X_9$, A_2BX_6?

(iii) Construct close-packed layers of the AX_3 type shown in figure 1.1. Stack them in the sequence ... AB .... Identify octahedral sites surrounded by six X atoms. Fill these 'X_6 sites' with smaller atoms B to form structures of stoicheiometry ABX_3, $A_3B_2X_9$, A_2BX_6.

* Glass beads 10 mm. in diameter are suitable.

What fraction of the total number of octahedral sites in the crystal is occupied in each case? Which of these three $A_nB_mX_{3n}$ structures contain discrete B_mX_{3n} ions?

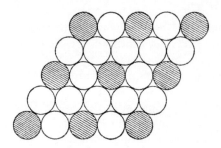

Figure 1.1. Close-packing of equal spheres of two kinds (AX_3).

Compare the models made above with the known structures of $RbCaF_3$, $Cs_3Tl_2Cl_9$ and K_2SiF_6.

1.4 Structures Based on Octahedral Coordination

This experiment requires octahedra of expanded polystyrene (p. 5). Each octahedron represents an AB_6 unit, A being at the centre of the solid and B_{1-6} at the apices.

(i) Octahedra can be joined by sharing vertices, edges or faces. Write down the formulae for compounds formed by joining $2, 3, 4, \ldots, n$ octahedra linearly in each of these three ways.

Now look up the structures of the following compounds and make models of them using octahedra:

$$[Tl_2Cl_9]^{3-}; \ MoI_3; \ NbI_4; \ K_2HgCl_4 \cdot 2H_2O; \ Ru_2Cl_{10}O; \ Tl_2AlF_5.$$

(ii) If more than two octahedral units are shared, many complex structures may be readily represented. We consider here the sharing of vertices and edges only; the sharing of faces is rare (why?).

(a) Sharing of more than two vertices: make models of the structures of ReO_3 and PdF_3. Compare these models with those of the same compounds made from close-packed layers of spheres with octahedral sites filled.

What is the relationship between ReO_3 and the perovskites?

(b) Make a model of the BiI_3 layer structure by sharing three edges of each octahedron in the most symmetrical manner. Compare this with a model of BiI_3 made from close-packed spheres.

(c) If two linear chains of octahedra, formed by sharing opposite edges, are themselves joined together laterally (see figure 1.2), what is the composition AX_n of the resulting structure? Compare your model with the structures of NH_4CdCl_3 and CdI_2.

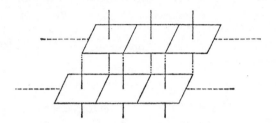

Figure 1.2. The lateral joining of two linear chains of octahedra.

(iii) The iso- and heteropolyacids of molybdenum and tungsten consist basically of MO_6 octahedra joined together by sharing vertices or edges. In the heteropolyacids a hetero atom, A, is found in the centre of an AO_6 octahedron in the middle of the complex ion. Following the illustrations in the references below, make models of the following ions from polystyrene octahedra and tetrahedra:

$$[Mo_7O_{24}]^{6-}; \ [Mo_8O_{26}]^{4-}; \ [TeMo_6O_{24}]^{6-}; \ [MnMo_9O_{32}]^{6-};$$

$$[PW_{12}O_{40}]^{3-}; \ [PW_{18}O_{62}]^{6-}.$$

References

1. A. F. Wells, *Structural Inorganic Chemistry*, 3rd edition, Oxford, 1962.
2. F. A. Cotton and G. Wilkinson, *Advanced Inorganic Chemistry*, Interscience, New York, 1962.

1.5 Structures Based on Tetrahedral Coordination

This experiment requires the use of tetrahedra of expanded polystyrene (p. 5). Each solid tetrahedron represents an AB_4 unit having a central atom, A, to which are coordinated four other atoms, B, with their centres at the apices of the solid.

(i) Tetrahedra may be joined by sharing faces, edges or vertices. Work out the internuclear distances, A–A, between the central atoms in tetrahedra when joined in each of these ways. No structure is found in nature corresponding to the joining of two or more tetrahedra by sharing faces. Why?

(ii) Several halides, A_2X_6, can be represented by joining two tetrahedra by a common edge, e.g., Al_2Cl_6. If a large chain is made up in this way, the resulting structure is that of SiS_2. In Al_2Cl_6, the shared edge is shorter than the other polyhedral edges. Why? Discuss the structures of Al_2Cl_6 and SiS_2 from the viewpoint of Pauling's Rules (L. Pauling, *The Nature of the Chemical Bond*, 3rd edition, Oxford, 1960, p. 543 ff).

(iii) Make models of the following by joining tetrahedra in appropriate ways:

$$\gamma\text{-}SO_3; \quad [P_4O_{12}]^{4-}; \quad P_4O_{10}(g); \quad K_2CuCl_3; \quad CsCu_2Cl_3; \quad \text{red } HgI_2$$

How many vertices does each tetrahedron share in each of these structures? Compare the structures of the two copper complexes with that of $CsCuCl_3$.

1.6 Silicates

The structures of silicates are most clearly visualized by considering them as built up from SiO_4 tetrahedra. Vertices only are shared. Using polystyrene tetrahedra and following the diagrams in references 1–3, construct models of the following:

(i)   The cyclic anion $Si_3O_9^{6-}$ or $(SiO_3^{2-})_3$.
(ii) The cyclic anion $(SiO_3^{2-})_6$, found in *beryl*.
(iii) The linear chain $(SiO_3^{2-})_n$ of *diopside*, a pyroxene. Stack several chains together as in figure 1.3 and note the planes of cleavage.
(iv) A double chain of the *amphibole* type.

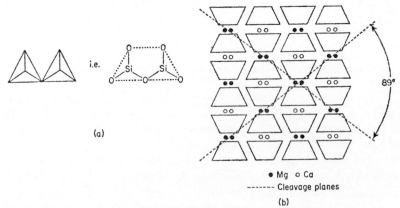

(a)

(b)

● Mg o Ca
------- Cleavage planes

Figure 1.3. The structure of diopside: (a) detail of one chain; (b) method of packing and planes of cleavage.

(v)   *Tridymite* and *cristobalite*, two of the forms of silica. Use about 16 tetrahedra for each model.

(vi)   A portion of the chain of a *fibrous zeolite*.

(vii)   A portion of a common *felspar* lattice.

Using truncated octahedra of polystyrene (p. 5), show that they can be packed to fill all space. If each vertex of the polyhedron is taken to represent a silicon atom, then this model forms the basis of the structure of the zeolite, *chabazite*. Make a ball-and-spring model of the silicon–oxygen framework represented by a single truncated octahedron (reference 2, figure 291) and compare both models with a model of chabazite built up from tetrahedra (reference 2, figure 289c).

By interspersing the truncated octahedra with cubes (reference 2, figure 31b), the basic framework of a further series of aluminosilicates can be represented.[4]

References

1. F. A. Cotton and G. Wilkinson, *Advanced Inorganic Chemistry*, Interscience, New York, 1962.
2. A. F. Wells, *Structural Inorganic Chemistry*, 3rd edition, Oxford, 1962.
3. W. E. Addison, *Structural Principles in Inorganic Compounds*, Longmans, London, 1961.
4. R. H. E. Duffet and G. J. Minkoff, *Discovery*, December 1964; D. W. Breck, *J. Chem. Educ.*, 1964, **41**, 678.

Chapter 2

The Stoicheiometry of Reactions
by Volumetric Methods

The aim of the following experiments is to determine the stoicheiometry of a series of oxidation–reduction reactions using standard solutions. From observations during the titration, or from subsequent tests on the solution, it is possible to determine the products of oxidation and the equivalent weights of the reacting species. Finally, the equation for the reaction can be deduced.

Equivalent weights and redox equations

The best method of writing and balancing equations, as well as deducing equivalent weights, is the ion–electron method. This is described below.

By definition, the *equivalent weight* of an oxidizing or reducing agent is that weight of reagent which reacts with or liberates 1·008 g. of available hydrogen or 8·000 g. of available oxygen. The equation

$$H \rightleftharpoons H^+ + e^-$$

indicates that a hydrogen atom can be considered as splitting into a proton plus an electron. Thus, instead of considering the hypothetical number of hydrogen or oxygen atoms taking part in a reaction (e.g., treating $K_2Cr_2O_7$ as if it were $K_2O + Cr_2O_3 + 3\,[O]$), one need only consider the number of *electrons* taking part. That electrons do take part in redox reactions can be shown by considering the Daniel cell. Zinc metal at one electrode is oxidized to zinc cations

$$Zn^0 \rightleftharpoons Zn^{2+} + 2\,e^-$$

with liberation of electrons. At the other electrode, cupric ions are reduced to copper metal

$$Cu^{2+} + 2\,e^- \rightleftharpoons Cu^0$$

with the absorption of electrons. Thus, on connecting the electrodes externally, a current flows, proving that electrons have taken part in the oxidation and reduction. It follows also that, *in this reaction*, the equivalent weights of the copper and of the zinc are one half of the atomic weights.

The solvent frequently takes part in redox reactions and any equation written to represent such a reaction must include H_2O, H^+ or OH^- species. The use of one or more of these species is often necessary to balance reactions. Thus, iodate can be reduced to I^+ (in concentrated acid), the partial ionic equation for the reaction being

$$IO_3^- + 6\,H^+ + 4\,e^- \rightarrow I^+ + 3\,H_2O$$

The reduction of iodate must involve reaction with protons in solution – either from the acid added or from the solvent. The equivalent weight of iodate in this reaction is one quarter of the formula weight because four electrons are involved for each iodate ion reduced.

Procedure for determination of stoicheiometry

The equation for the reaction between potassium permanganate and oxalic acid can be deduced by means of the following sequence. Apart from the titration figures, the only information needed is a knowledge of the reduction product of the permanganate ion and the oxidation product of the oxalate ion.

Step 1 Oxidizing agent: MnO_4^- reduced to Mn^{2+}.

Step 2 Reducing agent: $(COO)_2^{2-}$ oxidized to CO_2 gas.

Step 3 Write the *partial ionic equation* for the oxidizing agent. Incorporate H_2O, H^+ or OH^- if necessary, and check that it balances chemically and electrically.

$$MnO_4^- + 8\,H^+ + 5\,e^- \rightarrow Mn^{2+} + 4\,H_2O \tag{1}$$

Step 4 Repeat step 3 for the reducing agent.

$$(COO)_2^{2-} \rightarrow 2\,CO_2 + 2\,e^- \tag{2}$$

Step 5 To obtain the *overall ionic equation* for the reaction, add together the two partial ionic equations. Multiply each equation by a factor, if necessary, so that the number of electrons on each side cancels out. In this case multiply (1) by 2 and (2) by 5, thus:

$$2\,MnO_4^- + 16\,H^+ + 10\,e^- \rightarrow 2\,Mn^{2+} + 8\,H_2O$$
$$5\,(COO)_2^{2-} \rightarrow 10\,CO_2 + 10\,e^-$$
$$2\,MnO_4^- + 5\,(COO)_2^{2-} + 16\,H^+ \rightarrow 2\,Mn^{2+} + 10\,CO_2 + 8\,H_2O$$

This is the overall ionic equation and it must be consistent with the titration figures. Experimentally it is found that two moles of potassium permanganate are exactly equivalent to five moles of oxalic acid, thus confirming the deductions.

It is unnecessary to put into the equations ions which take no part in the reaction, e.g., K^+. The equivalent weights of permanganate and oxalate can be deduced from the partial ionic equations (1) and (2). The equivalent weight of the permanganate, i.e., $KMnO_4$, is one fifth of the molecular weight because one molecule is equivalent to five electrons. The equivalent weight of the oxalic acid is one half the molecular weight because one molecule is equivalent to two electrons.

Questions

In certain titrations, an excess of one solution is added to react with all the other solution. The excess solution is back titrated. Does it matter *how much* excess is added? Is it more accurate to add a large or small excess? (Consider sources of error.)

References

1. H. R. Tietze, *J. Chem. Educ.*, 1963, **40**, 344.
2. D. N. Grindley, *An Advanced Course in Practical Inorganic Chemistry*, Butterworths, London, 1964, p. 117.

2.1 The Reaction between Ferrous Ions and Potassium Permanganate

Solutions required: approximately M/20 ferrous ammonium sulphate
approximately M/100 potassium permanganate
(both standardized)

Titration

To 25 ml. M/20 ferrous solution add 25 ml. dilute sulphuric acid and titrate with M/100 potassium permanganate until a pink colouration just persists. Save the resulting solution for test 2 below. Repeat to obtain consistent titres.

Deductions

1. What is the ratio of your titration figures, corrected to the same molarity? From this, deduce x and y in the equation

$$x\ Fe^{2+} + y\ MnO_4^- \rightarrow products$$

2. Test the resulting solution (saved from the titration) with potassium ferrocyanide. What is observed, and what conclusions can you draw about the products of oxidation?

3. What is the reduction product of the permanganate?

4. Deduce the partial ionic equations for the oxidant and reductant and balance chemically and electrically

$$Fe^{2+} \rightarrow Fe^{?+}$$

$$MnO_4^- \rightarrow ?$$

5. Complete the overall ionic equation in (1) above. Do your titration figures confirm your deductions?

6. What are the equivalent weights of potassium permanganate and the ferrous salt in terms of their molecular weights?

2.2 The Reaction between Copper Metal and Ferric Ions

Materials required: pure copper powder
approximately M/5 ferric sulphate solution
standardized M/25 potassium permanganate solution

Titration

Weigh out accurately about 0·15 g. copper powder and add 25 ml. of the approximately M/5 ferric solution (i.e., in excess) and 25 ml. dilute sulphuric acid. Boil the solution gently until the copper has dissolved. Cool and oxidize the ferrous ion produced by titration with potassium permanganate (M/25). Repeat with another copper sample.

Deductions

1. From the potassium permanganate titration figure, deduce the number of moles of ferric solution that had been reduced to ferrous by the copper.

2. Convert to moles the weight of copper taken.

3. From (1) and (2) deduce the mole ratio of the reactants in the following equation

$$x \, Cu^0 + y \, Fe^{3+} \rightarrow y \, Fe^{2+} + x \, Cu^{?+}$$

4. Complete the equation by balancing chemically and electrically.

5. What is the equivalent weight of the copper metal in this reaction?

2.3 The Reaction between Potassium Dichromate and Iron

Materials required: pure iron wire
approximately $M/50$ potassium dichromate, standardized

Titration

Weigh out accurately $0 \cdot 1$–$0 \cdot 15$ g. of iron wire and dissolve it in 100 ml. dilute sulphuric acid in a conical flask. Add about 1 g. sodium bicarbonate to expel the air and loosely stopper the flask. Add barium diphenylamine sulphonate indicator and 5 ml. syrupy phosphoric acid. Titrate with potassium dichromate until the indicator shows the first permanent tinge of blue-violet. Save the resulting solution for test 3 below. Repeat with another sample of iron.

Deductions

1. From your titration figure calculate the weight of potassium dichromate used in each titration.
2. Deduce x and y in the equation

$$x\,\mathrm{Fe}^{2+} + y\,\mathrm{Cr_2O_7^{2-}} \rightarrow ?$$

3. To what is the iron oxidized? Test your final solution (saved from the titration) with potassium ferrocyanide.
4. What is the dichromate reduced to?
5. Deduce the partial ionic equations for the oxidant and reductant, and balance the equations chemically and electrically.

$$\mathrm{Fe}^{2+} \rightarrow \mathrm{Fe}^{?+}$$

$$\mathrm{Cr_2O_7^{2-}} \rightarrow ?$$

6. Complete the overall ionic equation in (2) above. Do your titration figures and subsequent calculation of mole ratios confirm your deductions?
7. What is the equivalent weight of the potassium dichromate in this reaction?
8. What rôle does phosphoric acid play in the titration?

2.4 The Reaction between Ceric Ions and Hydrogen Peroxide

Solutions required: approximately M/50 ceric ammonium nitrate (or
sulphate) dissolved in sulphuric acid
approximately M/50 hydrogen peroxide
(both solutions standardized)

Titration

Titrate 10 ml. M/50 hydrogen peroxide with M/50 ceric solution
using ferroin as indicator (colour change is red to blue, the end-point
being the last trace of purple). Barium diphenylamine sulphonate can
also be used as indicator. Repeat to give consistent titres.

Deductions

1. What is the ratio of your titration figures, corrected to the same
molarity? From this, deduce x and y in the equation

$$x \; Ce^{4+} + y \; H_2O_2 \rightarrow products$$

2. On a test-tube scale, add some solid ceric salt to bench hydrogen
peroxide. What gas is evolved?
3. From a consideration of the chemistry of cerium, state what
oxidation state the Ce^{4+} has been reduced to?
4. Deduce the partial ionic equations for the oxidant and reductant
and balance each chemically and electrically.

$$Ce^{4+} \rightarrow Ce^{?+}$$

$$H_2O_2 \rightarrow ?$$

5. Complete the overall ionic equation in (1) above. Do your
titration figures confirm your deductions?
6. What are the equivalent weights of hydrogen peroxide and the
ceric salt in terms of their molecular weights?

2.5 The Reaction between Arsenious Oxide and Potassium Bromate

Solutions required: approximately M/100 potassium bromate
approximately M/100 arsenious oxide in sodium
hydroxide
(both solutions standardized)

Titration

To 25 ml. $\text{M}/100$ arsenious oxide solution (measured by burette –
poisonous) add 5 ml. concentrated sulphuric acid and methyl orange
or methyl red indicator. Titrate very slowly with $\text{M}/100$ potassium
bromate until the indicator is just bleached. Save the resulting solution for test 2 below. With this irreversible oxidation indicator, its
destruction may be a little premature and additional indicator will
be needed near the end-point. Immediate discharge of colour on
further addition of indicator shows that the equivalence point has
been passed. Repeat the titration to give consistent titres.

Deductions

1. What is the ratio of your titration figures, corrected to the same
molarity? From this deduce x and y in the equation

$$x \, BrO_3^- + y \, As_2O_3 \rightarrow products$$

2. Test the resulting solution, saved from the titration, with silver
nitrate. To what has the bromate been reduced?

3. From a consideration of the stable valencies of arsenic, state to
what oxide the As_2O_3 has been oxidized.

4. Deduce the partial ionic equations for the oxidant and the
reductant and balance each chemically and electrically

$$BrO_3^- \rightarrow ?$$
$$As_2O_3 \rightarrow ?$$

5. Complete the overall ionic equation in (1) above. Do your titration figures confirm your deductions?

6. What are the equivalent weights of potassium bromate and
arsenious oxide in terms of their molecular weights?

7. How does the indicator work?

> NOTE   In alkaline solution, arsenious oxide forms sodium
> arsenite, Na_3AsO_3, and so to be strictly correct, one should
> consider the oxidation of AsO_3^{3-}. The stoicheiometry is not
> affected by considering the anion AsO_3^{3-} as As_2O_3. Sodium
> arsenite cannot be obtained in a suitable state of purity for
> titrations.

2.6 The Reaction between Ferrocyanide and Bromate Ions

Solutions required: approximately $\text{M}/50$ potassium ferrocyanide
                      approximately $\text{M}/100$ potassium bromate
                      (both standardized)

Titration

To 50 ml. M/50 potassium ferrocyanide solution (measured by burette – poisonous) add 5 ml. concentrated hydrochloric acid and methyl orange or methyl red indicator. Titrate very slowly with M/100 potassium bromate until the indicator is just bleached. Additional indicator will be needed near the end-point because of premature bleaching – see experiment 2.5. Save the resulting solution for test 2 below. Repeat the titration to give consistent titres.

Deductions

1.   What is the ratio of your titration figures, corrected to the same molarity? From this, deduce x and y in the equation

$$x \, BrO_3^- + y \, [Fe(CN)_6]^{4-} \rightarrow products$$

2.   Test the resulting solution saved from the titration with ferrous sulphate solution – what is observed and what can be deduced from your observation?
3.   To what is the bromate reduced?
4.   Deduce the partial ionic equations for the oxidant and reductant and balance each chemically and electrically.

$$BrO_3^- \rightarrow ?$$

$$[Fe(CN)_6]^{4-} \rightarrow ?$$

5.   Complete the overall ionic equation (1) above. Do the titration figures confirm your deductions?
6.   What are the equivalent weights of potassium bromate and potassium ferrocyanide in terms of their molecular weights?

2.7 The Reaction between Hydrazinium Ions and Potassium Iodate

Solutions required: approximately M/20 hydrazine sulphate
                               approximately M/20 potassium iodate
                               (both standardized)

Titration

To 25 ml. M/20 hydrazine sulphate solution, add 25 ml. concentrated hydrochloric acid and 5 ml. chloroform or carbon tetrachloride. Titrate this with M/20 potassium iodate with vigorous shaking until the organic layer loses its purple colour and becomes almost colourless. Repeat to obtain consistent titres.

4

Deductions

1.　What is the ratio of your titration figures, corrected to the same molarity? From this deduce x and y in the equation

$$x \, IO_3^- + y \, N_2H_4 \rightarrow products$$

2.　What gas is evolved? If necessary, test on a small scale using much stronger solutions.

3.　The iodate is reduced to I^+ in this reaction. Deduce the partial ionic equations for the oxidizing and the reducing agent. Balance chemically and electrically.

$$IO_3^- \rightarrow I^+$$

$$N_2H_4 \rightarrow \, ?$$

4.　Complete the overall ionic equations in (1) above. Do the titration figures confirm your conclusions?

5.　What are the equivalent weights of hydrazine and potassium iodate in terms of their molecular weights?

6.　If the iodate is reduced to I^+, how do you account for the fact that iodine is produced during the reaction?

7.　How does potassium iodate react in dilute acid solution and what is its equivalent weight under these conditions?

Chapter 3

More Advanced Techniques
and Measurements

3.1 Flame Photometry: Solubility of a Precipitate

In quantitative analysis the precipitation of calcium as its oxalate
is generally assumed to be complete. This experiment is designed to
find out the extent to which the assumption is justified.

The method depends upon the accurate determination of low concentrations of calcium in solution; for this a flame photometer is
used to produce, and measure the intensity of, the visible emission
spectra of excited metal atoms. In the instrument a fine spray of a
solution of the sample is passed through a coal-gas flame. Radiation
from the flame is passed through a lens and appropriate filters to a
photocell. The intensity of the radiation is displayed on a galvanom-
eter, the deflection of which is proportional to the concentration of
sample in the solution. For the method of use of the instrument, see
the manufacturer's instructions.

Procedure

1. Precipitate calcium oxalate from a solution of calcium chloride
as follows. Acidify with dilute hydrochloric acid, warm to 70°c and
add ammonium oxalate. Neutralize the solution by slow addition of
dilute ammonium hydroxide. Cool to room temperature (record it)
and filter. The filtrate will contain a saturated solution of calcium
oxalate.
2. Prepare a standard solution of calcium by dissolving about 2·5 g.
pure calcium carbonate, accurately weighed, in dilute hydrochloric
acid. Dilute to 1 litre with water. Dilute 50 ml., 25 ml. and 10 ml.
portions of this solution to 1 litre each to give solutions containing,
respectively, 50, 25, and 10 p.p.m. of calcium. (A stock solution of
2·4973 g./l. calcium carbonate contains 1 g. calcium.)

3. Use the standard solutions for calibration of the flame photometer and then determine the calcium content of your oxalate solution. From your results, calculate the solubility of calcium oxalate in water.

To what extent does this result affect the accuracy of the quantitative determination of calcium as its oxalate?

3.2 Solvent Extraction: Preparation of 12-Tungstosilicic Acid, $H_4SiW_{12}O_{40} \cdot 7 H_2O$

The technique of solvent extraction finds widespread use in inorganic chemistry. Water-soluble hydrated inorganic complexes or salts can frequently be made to complex with (usually) organic reagents to form either an uncharged complex or one with hydrophobic groups. They then become soluble in solvents with lower dielectric constants. Thus, by selectively complexing a mixture of compounds, separation can be achieved by extraction with an appropriate solvent. An example of this is the extraction of plutonium and uranium from fission products by treatment with tributylphosphate. The $(UO_2)^{2+}$ and Pu^{4+} ions complex with tributylphosphate, TBP, in the presence of nitric acid to form, for example, $UO_2(NO_3)_2 \cdot 2\,TBP$, which is then soluble in carbon tetrachloride and can thus be extracted. The fission products do not complex and remain in the aqueous layer.

Procedure

Dissolve 12 g. sodium tungstate, $Na_2WO_4 \cdot 2 H_2O$, in 25 ml. water and add 0·93 g. sodium silicate solution (i.e., water glass, d. 1·38 g./ml.). Vigorously stir the solution at just below the boiling point and add 8 ml. concentrated hydrochloric acid dropwise over a period of 30 min. from a dropping funnel. Cool the solution and filter it, then add a further 5 ml. concentrated hydrochloric acid slowly. Shake the solution in a separating funnel with 10 ml. ether and, if three layers do not form, add a little more ether. Withdraw the bottom oily layer containing the ether complex and save it in a beaker. Add a further 10 ml. ether to the liquid in the separating funnel, shake well and draw off the bottom layer again. Repeat this several times to extract the yellow product in the middle layer into the lower ether–oil layer. Rinse out the separating funnel and return the ether complex to the funnel together with a solution of 3 ml. concentrated hydrochloric acid in 10 ml. water and 4 ml. ether. After shaking the mixture run the lower layer into an evaporating dish and allow the ether to evaporate. Dry the almost colourless crystals produced at 70°c for 2 hr. Do not touch the crystals with a metal spatula, or they will turn blue.

Determination of the equivalent weight

Weigh out about 2 g. of the heteropoly acid and dissolve in water. Titrate the acid with N/10 sodium hydroxide using methyl orange (or, preferably, chlorophenol red) as indicator. What is the basicity of the acid?

Questions

1. Why do the crystals turn blue when a metal spatula touches them?
2. Draw the structure of the complex and make a model of it using expanded polystyrene octahedra (see experiment 1.4). How many structurally different kinds of oxygen atom are there in the anion and how many oxygen atoms of each kind are there?

References

1. E. O. North, *Inorg. Synth.*, **1**, 129.
2. D. L. Kepert, *Progr. Inorg. Chem.*, 1962, **4**, 199.

3.3 Ion Exchange: Separation of Halides

The ion-exchange resin used in this experiment (Deacidite FF, 50–200 mesh) is an insoluble cross-linked polymer containing substituted quarternary ammonium groups. It is supplied in the chloride form, i.e., the anion associated with the quarternary nitrogen atom is chloride. The function of an ion-exchange resin depends upon a chemical equilibrium which may be represented as:

$$RCl + NO_3^- \rightleftharpoons RNO_3 + Cl^-$$

Hence, a concentrated solution of a nitrate will force the equilibrium to the right and will gradually wash the chloride off the column. Due to the differences in concentration of the two anions as the process continues, the equilibrium will be at different positions at different parts of the column. The process must be carried out reasonably slowly to allow equilibrium to be established.

Ion-exchange methods are widely used in preparation and analysis, an important application being the separation of the lanthanide and actinide elements. In this experiment you separate a mixture of chloride and bromide. This process is quantitative. Both anions readily exchange with the nitrate on the column when a solution containing them is poured down the column. They are then eluted from the column by an excess of sodium nitrate solution, bromide being retained more tenaciously than chloride. The progress of the separation can be followed by titrating 10 ml. portions of eluent with standard silver nitrate.

1. *Preparation of column*

Suspend 40 g. of the resin in distilled water, allow it to settle and decant the fine suspension. Repeat the procedure with further portions of distilled water until the resin settles quickly leaving a clear supernatant liquid. Pour a slurry of the resin into a column (approximately 15 cm. long; ideally, the ratio of length to diameter should be 12 : 1) and insert a separating funnel into the top of the tube. Wash* the column with 200 ml. dilute nitric acid and test the eluent until it gives no reaction for chloride with silver nitrate. Displace the nitric acid by pouring through the column 50 ml. of 0·3 M sodium nitrate, the solvent which will be used to elute the chloride from the column.

> NOTE   1. If your column has been used before start at *
> above.
> 2. *Never* allow the column to become dry. Stopper the end
> when it is left.

2. *Separation*

Weigh out accurately about 0·1 g. sodium chloride and 0·2 g. potassium bromide and dissolve them in 2 ml. water. Transfer the solution to the top of the column and ensure complete transference by washing out the beaker several times with 0·3 M sodium nitrate. Put 0·3 M sodium nitrate solution in the separating funnel and adjust the rate of flow through the funnel to about 1 ml. per min. Collect the eluate in 10 ml. measuring cylinders and titrate each 10 ml. portion with a standard solution of silver nitrate (approx. 0·05 N). A blank titration should be carried out against 10 ml. of the sodium nitrate solution, taking care to add the same amount of potassium chromate as indicator each time. Plot titre against millilitres eluted, and when the titre falls to approximately zero, denoting that all the chloride has been recovered, change the eluent to 0·6 M sodium nitrate to remove the bromide. Titrate each fraction as before and carry out a new blank on the 0·6 M solution. By summing the titres at each stage calculate the recovery of both chloride and bromide. If the titre does not fall exactly to zero, a correction must be made from the graph where the two curves overlap. Remember to allow for the blank in plotting all the titration values.

Questions

1. Why is bromide held by the column more tenaciously than chloride?
2. Could this experiment be adapted for the separation of fluoride, chloride, bromide and iodide?
3. How would you de-ionize tap water?

3.4 Ion Exchange: Preparation of Triphosphoric Acid, $H_5P_3O_{10}$

The fusion of simple phosphates produces condensed linear and cyclic phosphates, the chain length depending upon the conditions. The method given below produces a product which is mainly a linear triphosphate: the free acid can only be prepared on an ion-exchange resin. The method also lends itself to the determination of the average chain length.

Preparation of penta-sodium triphosphate (sodium tripoly-phosphate), $Na_5P_3O_{10}$

Heat a well ground mixture of 1·6 g. $NaH_2PO_4 \cdot 2 H_2O$ and 7·4 g. of $Na_2HPO_4 \cdot 12 H_2O$ in a platinum (or nickel) crucible for two hours at 540–580°C. Allow to cool in air. If other hydrates are used, calculate the weights so that the mole ratio of $NaH_2PO_4 : Na_2HPO_4$ is 1 : 2.

Preparation of triphosphoric acid, $H_5P_3O_{10}$

Prepare a cation-exchange resin column (using Dowex 50 or Amberite 225, 20–50 mesh) as described in experiment 3.3. Convert the resin to the hydrogen form by allowing 500 ml. dilute hydrochloric acid to percolate through it. Remove the acid by running water through the column until no chloride is detected.

Weigh out about 0·2 g. penta-sodium triphosphate, $Na_5P_3O_{10}$, and dissolve it in 50 ml. water. Allow this solution to percolate through the column followed by 200 ml. water and collect the free acid produced in a beaker.

Determination of average chain length

Dip the electrode of a pH meter into 150–200 ml. of the above solution and titrate with 0·05 N sodium hydroxide. Record the pH of the solution after each 1 ml. of alkali has been added (more frequently at end-points). Plot the pH against volume of sodium hydroxide added.

In any linear polyphosphoric acid, $H(PO_3H)_nOH$, there are n strongly acidic protons per chain (one per phosphorus atom) and two weakly acidic protons per chain (one at each end). Thus, from the titration curve, the first end-point, about pH 4–5, represents the ionization of the n strongly acidic protons and the second and third end-points, about pH 7–8 and 9–10, represent the two terminal weakly acid protons. The ratio of the titration figures thus gives the average chain length.

Questions

1. How would you separate a mixture of sodium polyphosphates of differing chain length ?
2. How would you distinguish a cyclic polyphosphate from a linear polyphosphate ?

Reference

E. J. Griffith, *J. Amer. Soc.*, 1957, **79**, 509.

3.5 Paper Chromatography

Partition chromatography is a counter-current distribution technique which depends upon the partition of a solute between a mobile phase and a stationary phase. The stationary phase, water, is held on a *support*, which can be any hydrated solid, e.g., silica gel or cellulose. In practice, it is usually good-quality filter paper. The solvent used to separate the solute components is called the *eluant*. The process of separating is called *development*. The movement of the solutes with respect to the eluant is measured by the R_f value.

$$R_f = \frac{\text{Rate of movement of solvent}}{\text{Rate of movement of solute}}$$

The solvent composition, especially the water content, is critical.

1. Separation of chloride, bromide and iodide

Fill a boiling tube to a depth of 2 cm. with an eluant consisting of 5 parts acetone and 1 part water. Stopper the tube and allow the air inside to become saturated with solvent vapour. Apply a drop of the solution to be analysed (using a drawn-out capillary or melting-point tube) about 1 cm. from the lower end of a strip of 1 cm. wide filter paper (Whatman No. 1). Mark the position of the drop with a pencil line. Apply sufficient solution to spread to about 0·5 cm. diameter. A convenient strength of solution is about M/10, using the sodium salts of the halides. Insert the strip into the boiling tube so that the lower end just dips into the liquid. Hold the upper end between the two halves of a split cork fitting into the neck of the boiling tube (figure 3.1). Take care that the paper is kept clean by

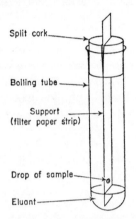

Figure 3.1. Qualitative paper chromatography.

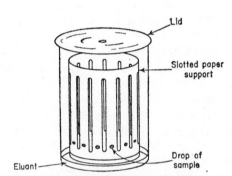

Figure 3.2. Semi-quantitative paper chromatography.

keeping handling to a minimum. Never allow the sides of the paper to come in contact with the walls of the boiling tube.

Allow the chromatogram to develop until the rising solvent front is near the cork. Remove the strip and mark the position of the solvent front. Dry the chromatogram in air and then moisten it with silver nitrate solution on a watch glass. Remove excess silver nitrate by dipping the chromatogram for 30 sec. in a beaker of nearly boiling water. Then spray with hydrogen sulphide gas and dry.

Measure the R_f values for each band.

Questions
1. Which halide ion travels fastest? Why?
2. How would you detect fluoride if this had been present?

2. Semi-quantitative separation of cobalt and nickel

Prepare five solutions containing respectively 0·2 M, 0·1 M, 0·05 M, 0·025 M and 0·0125 M cobalt and nickel chlorides. A solution containing cobalt and nickel chlorides of unknown strength is provided.

Use Whatman slotted paper (Pattern CRL/1, Grade 1) and draw a pencil line just above the lower end of the slots. Put equal volumes of each of these solutions (the unknown in duplicate) onto the line using a capillary tube as in (1). Each drop can now develop up a strip of the paper without interfering with its neighbours. Bend the sheet into a cylinder with a paper clip at the top and insert it into a 600 ml. beaker containing 25 ml. of the solvent. This consists of 7·5 parts of concentrated hydrochloric acid, 4 parts of water and 37·5 parts of methyl ethyl ketone (see figure 3.2). Cover the beaker with a lid.

When the eluant has nearly reached the top of the slots, remove the chromatogram and stand it in a dry covered beaker containing a small beaker of concentrated ammonium hydroxide. Spray the chromatogram on both sides, either with hydrogen sulphide gas *or* with a freshly prepared solution containing equal volumes of rubeanic acid and 1 : 1 ammonium hydroxide.

Compare the intensities of the spots from the unknown solutions with those of the standards and thus determine the cobalt and nickel content. Record the R_f values.

References

1. F. H. Pollard and J. F. W. McOmie, *Chromatographic Methods of Inorganic Analysis*, Butterworths, London, 1953.
2. A. I. Vogel, *Quantitative Inorganic Analysis*, 3rd edition, Longmans, London, 1961.

3.6 Measurement of the Ionization Potentials of the Rare Gases

If the potential difference between two electrodes in a gas-filled valve is increased slowly, only a very small current will pass until the potential reaches a critical value. This value is the ionization potential of the gas and electrons are now released from the atoms of the gas causing a larger current to flow suddenly. The circuit provided (figure 3.3) contains five valves each being filled with one of the rare gases in a state of high purity. Using this circuit, the first ionization potentials of the gases can be measured with reasonable accuracy.

Procedure

Switch to the valve containing the gas under consideration and allow 1 min. for the valves to warm up. Increase the potential across the valve electrodes using the coarse and fine current controls until the ammeter gives the first recommended reading (see Table 3.1). In the case of neon, this is 0·1 mA. Take care to use the correct current scale so that maximum sensitivity is obtained, and record the

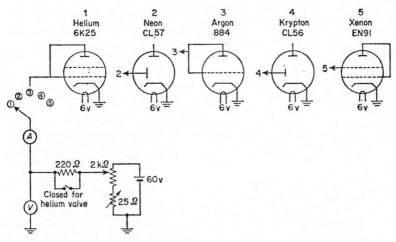

Figure 3.3. Basic circuit for measurement of ionization potentials.

voltage, V, corresponding to this current (using the best volts scale). Repeat this for larger currents and for other gases using the values recommended.

Table 3.1

Gas	Recommended range, mA	Intervals, mA
Helium	10–100	10
	110–150	10
	150–500	50
Neon	0·1–1·0	0·1
	1·2–2·0	0·2
	2·5–5·5	0·5
Argon	5–50	5
	50–90	10
Krypton	0·1–1·0	0·1
	1·2–3·0	0·2
Xenon	1–10	1
	12–40	2
	50–60	10

The Richardson equation states that the anode current, I, is proportional to $V^{3/2}$, i.e.,

$$I = k V^{3/2}$$

Plot a graph of $I^{2/3}$ against V for each gas and determine the potential at which the current suddenly increases.

Questions

1. How, and why, does the ionization potential vary down the group ?
2. How would you measure the ionization potential of (a) hydrogen gas, (b) nitrogen gas, and (c) sodium vapour. Describe the stages in the ionization of each.

Reference

B. E. Dineau and R. S. Nyholm, *J. Roy. Inst. Chem.*, 1963, **87**, 110.

Chapter 4

Group Chemistry: Reactions and Preparations of Compounds of s and p-Block Elements

Throughout this chapter emphasis is placed upon the chemistry of the s- and p-block elements and their compounds, not upon techniques; the latter will be dealt with in Section II.

Tests are given to be carried out on a readily available compound representative of the element. From observations of, e.g., colour changes, precipitation, gas evolution, etc., you should deduce the course of the reaction and try to explain all the observations. The aim of these tests is to illustrate:

(a) trends, within a group, of oxidation state or the relative stabilities within a particular class of compound,

(b) other properties of particular compounds which are of special importance or interest.

The tests are obviously not exhaustive of the chemistry of the elements concerned; discuss any extensions you wish to make with the demonstrator.

Following the Groups tests, there are usually one or two preparations. You should perform one of these and also the reactions indicated, which illustrate its chemistry. These preparations can mostly be carried out in one laboratory period (three hours); those which take longer can be conveniently left and continued another day.

For each preparation, record the weights of starting materials and the yield obtained. The percentage of the theoretical yield obtained, based on the significant starting material, should also be calculated. Keep samples of your compounds and label them with your name, the formula of the compound and the weight of material. Liquids or compounds unstable to air should be ampouled (see Appendix 2).

4.1 Group I

Reactions of lithium and group I

The chemistry of sodium and potassium should be familiar. Lithium, however, differs markedly in certain respects; the following tests illustrate some reactions of the element and comparisons with other elements.

Use lithium carbonate; for wet tests, dissolve a few milligrams in the minimum of dilute hydrochloric acid. Record all observations and interpret them as far as possible.

1. Examine the colour of the flame with a small spectroscope. Note the characteristic line (6703 Å). Compare the flame with those of sodium and potassium salts and also the colour when viewed through several thicknesses of cobalt blue glass. What causes spectral emission in the visible region?

2. Compare the reactions of *very small* pieces of lithium, sodium and potassium (careful!) metal with water. What reasons can you suggest for the differences in reactivity?

3. Add an excess of an ammoniacal solution of ammonium fluoride. What is the white gelatinous precipitate that is formed? Why does lithium behave differently from the other alkali metals in this respect?

4. Add an excess of an ammoniacal solution of ammonium or sodium carbonate to a concentrated solution of lithium salt. If no precipitate forms, allow to stand for half an hour. Why is lithium carbonate insoluble in water?

5. Separation of lithium from other group I elements: lithium and sodium are easily separated from the other alkali metals by the solubility of their perchlorates. Lithium can then be separated from sodium by making use of the solubility of lithium chloride in ethanol. The separation is best demonstrated with a mixture of lithium and potassium salts.

Take 0·1 g. each of lithium chloride and potassium chloride and add 5 ml. absolute alcohol. Stir for 2 min. and then filter the solution. Wash the residue twice with 1 ml. portions of alcohol and pass the washings through the same filter paper as before. Dissolve the residue in 2–3 ml. water. Test this solution for (a) potassium using 2 mg. sodium cobaltinitrite and (b) lithium. Evaporate the alcohol solution carefully to dryness. Dissolve the residue in 2–3 ml. water and test for potassium and lithium. Explain your observations.

4.2 Group II

Reactions of beryllium and group II

The chemistry of magnesium and calcium should be familiar. Beryllium differs in many of its properties and the following tests illustrate some reactions of the element.

For the following tests, use beryllium sulphate, calcium chloride and aluminium sulphate.

SAFETY NOTE   Beryllium compounds are very poisonous.

Record all observations and interpret them as far as possible.

1. Add dilute sodium hydroxide to solutions of beryllium, calcium and aluminium salts in water until a precipitate forms. Observe the effect of adding excess sodium hydroxide. Explain your observations.

2. Compare the colours of the flames of calcium, barium and strontium using a small spectroscope. What causes these spectra? Do not test the beryllium salt because of its toxicity.

3. Basic acetate test. Precipitate beryllium hydroxide with ammonium hydroxide and dissolve it in acetic acid. Evaporate to dryness and observe that the product dissolves in chloroform. The compound produced has the formula $Be_4O(OAc)_6$. What is its structure? Would you expect calcium to form such a compound?

4.3 Group III

Reactions of boron and aluminium

The chemistry of aluminium should be familiar. Boron differs markedly from aluminium in chemical properties and the following tests illustrate some of the differences.

For the following tests use sodium borate (borax) and boric acid.

1. Mix borax with an equal bulk of calcium fluoride and make into a thick paste with a drop of concentrated sulphuric acid. Hold some of the paste, on a platinum wire loop (or tip of a nickel spatula), just outside the base of a Bunsen flame. Observe the green flame (used as a test for borate) and explain the reaction.

2. Add one drop of concentrated sulphuric acid and 4 or 5 drops of methanol to sodium borate in a small porcelain crucible. Stir and then warm until the methanol catches fire. Observe the colour of the flame and explain the reactions which have taken place.

3. Prepare a concentrated solution of boric acid and divide it into two portions. To one portion add glycerol; test the acidity of both solutions with universal indicator paper (pH2·5–4). Comment on the result.

Do you think these reactions would take place also with aluminium?

Adducts of boron trifluoride

Boron trifluoride is a strong Lewis acid which readily forms addition compounds with Lewis bases, e.g., ether, water, ammonia.

SAFETY NOTE   Boron trifluoride is a corrosive gas which fumes in air. All operations must be carried out in a fume cupboard. Use rubber gloves and wash any spills off immediately since the compound slowly attacks rubber.

Preparation of adducts with ether and water*

Mix 6 g. boric oxide and 50 g. ammonium fluorborate (or 55 g. sodium fluorborate) in a 500 ml. two-necked round-bottom flask. Slowly add 45 ml. concentrated sulphuric acid from a dropping funnel and, when the initial vigorous reaction has died down, warm to maintain a steady reaction. Pass the mixture of boron trifluoride and hydrogen fluoride through a series of traps and bubblers, e.g., wash bottles. The first is reversed and empty and thus acts as a safety trap, the second contains 30 ml. concentrated sulphuric acid saturated with boric acid (to remove hydrogen fluoride). The third contains 30 ml. diethyl ether, cooled in ice, and the fourth a few millilitres of water, cooled in ice. Allow effluent gas to be drawn away by the draught of the fume cupboard or be absorbed in caustic soda (care!).

NOTE   All flasks, traps and tubes must be thoroughly dry before commencing the experiment.

Exercises

1. The fourth tube contains the dihydrate $BF_3 \cdot 2H_2O$ (m.p. 6°C). Test its reaction to litmus. How does it ionize?
2. Add 1 ml. pyridine to 10 ml. of the etherate solution. Filter the white adduct, wash with a little ether and allow it to dry. Heat the solid in a dry test tube. What happens? Does the adduct react with water?
3. Distil the etherate $BF_3 \cdot OEt_2$, and measure its boiling point (b.p. 125°C). Hydrolyse a portion and identify the products.
4. Why is boron trifluoride stable, but BH_3 unstable?

* Adapted from Walton, *Inorganic Preparations.*

Preparation of potassium tris(oxalato)aluminate, $K_3[Al(C_2O_4)_3] \cdot 3 H_2O$*

To 1 g. aluminium turnings slowly add 6 g. potassium hydroxide in 50 ml. water. When the effervescence subsides, heat the solution to boiling. Filter any residue. Add 14 g. oxalic acid crystals in several portions to the hot solution until the precipitate formed at first is just redissolved on continued boiling. Filter if necessary, cool to room temperature and add 50 ml. ethanol. Cool in ice, filter the crystals, wash with ethanol and dry in air.

Exercises

1. How does the complex react with acidified potassium permanganate at (a) room temperature and (b) 50°c ?
2. Analyse your compound on the basis of the above observations.
3. Draw the structure of the complex. What orbitals are involved ? Does boron form an analogous compound ?

Preparation of aluminium bromide, $AlBr_3$

Anhydrous aluminium bromide is a covalent compound and a weak Lewis acid.

SAFETY NOTE   This experiment must be carried out in a fume cupboard. The compound reacts violently with water; surplus material may be disposed of by reaction with alcohol.

Procedure

Put 6 g. aluminium turnings in a 250 ml. two-neck flask. Add dropwise from a separating funnel 13 ml. bromine at such a rate as to maintain a steady reaction. When the addition is complete distil the product directly into a receiving flask, the outlet of which is guarded with a phosphorus pentoxide drying tube. A second distillation over aluminium turnings may be necessary to obtain a colourless solid, m.p. 97·5°, b.p. 255°c.

Exercises

1. Dissolve some aluminium bromide in carbon disulphide and pass hydrogen sulphide gas through the solution. What is the product formed ?
2. What is the structure of aluminium bromide in the solid, liquid and vapour states ?
3. Devise a method of analysing this compound, and, with the approval of the demonstrator, determine the purity of your material.

* Adapted from Palmer, *Experimental Inorganic Chemistry.*

4.4 Group IV

Reactions of silicon, tin and lead

The following reactions illustrate the relative stabilities of the various oxidation states of these elements.

For the tests, use solutions of sodium silicate, stannous chloride, stannic chloride, lead acetate and red lead (dissolved in boiling dilute nitric acid and filtered – Pb^{IV}). Explain all observations.

1. Pass hydrogen sulphide into a solution of
   (a) sodium silicate,
   (b) acidified stannic chloride,
   (c) acidified stannous chloride,
   (d) Pb^{IV} solution,
   (e) acidified lead acetate.
2. Add 1 ml. ferric chloride solution to a solution of
   (a) stannous chloride,
   (b) lead(II) acetate.

Add to the resulting solution one drop of potassium ferricyanide.

What conclusions can you draw from (1) and (2) concerning the relative stabilities of various oxidation states?

Preparation of tris(acetylacetonato)silicon chloride hydrochloride and some derivatives

This large complex cation containing six-coordinated silicon can be used to stabilize ions such as $[FeCl_4]^-$ and $[ZnCl_3]^-$.

SAFETY NOTE   This experiment must be carried out in a fume cupboard.

Preparation of tris(acetylacetonato)silicon chloride hydrochloride, $[Si(acac)_3]Cl \cdot HCl$

Add a solution of 15 g. silicon tetrachloride in 40 ml. dry benzene, together with a chip of porous pot, to a 250 ml. two-neck flask equipped with a dropping funnel and a reflux condenser. The exits should be isolated from atmospheric moisture by calcium chloride drying tubes. Add dropwise 9 ml. acetylacetone in 20 ml. dry benzene with occasional agitation of the flask. Reflux the solution for 30 min. whereupon the yellow oily layer will change to a white solid. Filter the solid rapidly and wash three times with ether. Dry in a vacuum desiccator.

Derivatives

Prepare one of the following:

1. Tris(acetylacetonato)silicon tetrachloroferrate(III), [Si(acac)₃][FeCl₄]

Dissolve 3 g. tris(acetylacetonato)silicon chloride hydrochloride in 25 ml. chloroform and add 1·3 g. anhydrous ferric chloride. Gently shake the mixture until hydrogen chloride evolution ceases. Filter the solution and slowly add 50 ml. ether to the filtrate. After 15 min., filter the yellow-green crystals and wash them three times with dry ether.

2. Tris(acetylacetonato)silicon trichlorozincate, [Si(acac)₃][ZnCl₃]

Make a slurry of 1·2 g. dry zinc chloride in 10 ml. glacial acetic acid to which has been added 5 ml. acetic anhydride. Add 3 g. tris(acetylacetonato)silicon chloride hydrochloride and leave it to stand for 30 min. with occasional shaking. Filter the solid and dissolve it in the minimum of boiling dry chloroform. Precipitate the complex by adding twice its volume of dry ether and leave for 15 min. Filter the white solid and wash three times with ether.

Exercises

1. Devise a scheme for analysis of one of your compounds for silicon, ligand, chlorine and metal anion.
2. Discuss the stereochemistry of the complexes and calculate the 'spin only' magnetic moments of the iron and zinc derivatives.

Reference

R. F. Riley, R. West and R. Barbarin, *Inorg. Synth.*, **7**, 31.

Preparation of stannic chloride and stannic iodide and their adducts with triphenylphosphine

Prepare either stannic chloride or stannic iodide.

Stannic chloride, SnCl₄*

Put 5 g. granulated tin, cut into small pieces, in a 25 ml. semi-micro flask and add 13 ml. chlorosulphonic acid dropwise from a separating funnel. The rate should be sufficient to maintain a steady reaction. The heat of reaction is sufficient to distil the stannic chloride into the receiving flask (figure 4.1). When no further stannic chloride is produced, remove the receiving flask and redistil it, collecting the fraction boiling between 100° and 115°c.

* Adapted from Palmer, *Experimental Inorganic Chemistry.*

NOTE   Stannic chloride rapidly reacts with moisture from the air. Samples must be kept in a stoppered flask or ampouled.

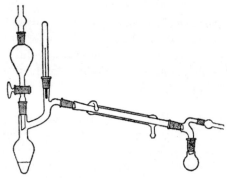

Figure 4.1. Apparatus for the preparation of stannic chloride.

*Stannic iodide, SnI₄**

Place 25 ml. glacial acetic acid and 25 ml. acetic anhydride in a 100 ml. round-bottom flask. Add 0·5 g. granulated tin cut into small pieces and 2 g. iodine. Reflux the contents gently on a sand-bath until a rather vigorous reaction begins. When this has subsided, boil the liquid until the violet vapour of iodine can no longer be seen. On cooling, orange crystals of stannic iodide separate. Filter these rapidly and recrystallize quickly from chloroform. Dry in a vacuum desiccator. Ampoule the product.

Triphenylphosphine adducts

(a) $SnCl_4 \cdot (PPh_3)_2$. Mix solutions of 1 g. stannic chloride in dry benzene and 2·1 g. triphenylphosphine in dry benzene. Filter and dry the precipitated adduct in a vacuum desiccator.

(b) $SnI_4 \cdot (PPh_3)_2$. Dissolve equimolar quantities of stannic iodide and triphenylphosphine separately in dry carbon tetrachloride. On mixing carefully, the adduct comes down over about 20 min. as dark crystals. Filter and dry in a vacuum desiccator.

Exercises

1. Analysis. (a) Tin. Hydrolyse a sample of tetrachloride or tetraiodide with dilute sulphuric acid. Precipitate hydrated stannic oxide with NH_4OH and then convert to anhydrous stannic oxide.

   (b) Determine iodine in tin tetraiodide by titration with potassium iodate in concentrated hydrochloric acid.

* Adapted from Palmer, *Experimental Inorganic Chemistry.*

2. Why are the stannic halides stabilized by complexing with phosphines?

3. Why are the triphenylphosphine adducts much more stable than the trialkylphosphine adducts? Why is the stability of the trialkylphosphine adducts (Cl > Br > I) apparently reversed with triarylphosphines? How would you investigate these phenomena?

Reference

J. A. C. Allison and F. G. Mann, *J. Chem. Soc.*, 1949, 2915.

4.5 Group V

Reactions of group V elements

1. *The elements.* (a) Place a little red phosphorus in a Pyrex test-tube, displace the air with a small piece of solid carbon dioxide and carefully heat the tube.

(b) Heat a little arsenious oxide with powdered charcoal and potassium cyanide in a dry test-tube. Comment on the reaction.

2. *Hydrides.* (a) Use salts of hydrazine and hydroxylamine and investigate the reaction of acidified solutions with (i) iodine, (ii) a titanic salt, (ii) a titanous salt, (iv) Fehling's solution.

(b) Place a small pellet of yellow phosphorus in an ignition tube and cover with concentrated sodium hydroxide. Warm gently. When all the phosphorus has reacted, neutralize the solution with dilute sulphuric acid and divide into four parts. (i) Add potassium permanganate dropwise, (ii) add silver nitrate solution, (iii) add copper sulphate solution, (iv) acidify and add zinc.

(c) Marsh's test. Place a little of any arsenic compound in a test-tube and cover with dilute sulphuric acid. Add solid carbon dioxide to displace the air and then granulated zinc. Immediately fit a delivery tube with a fine nozzle and, after a suitable time, try to ignite the gas coming out of the end. If it ignites, hold a porcelain surface in the flame and observe the formation of an arsenic mirror. In any case, note mirror formation when the delivery tube is heated. Test the solubility of the mirror in sodium hypochlorite solution. Repeat the test with antimony and bismuth compounds. Comment on the relative stabilities of these hydrides.

3. Compare the *oxidizing properties* of phosphate, arsenate, antimonate and bismuthate by using (a) a cold acidified manganous solution, (b) hydrogen sulphide.

4. Compare the *reducing properties* of nitrate, phosphite, arsenite, antimonite (Sb_2O_3 in dilute hydrochloric acid) by using (a) cold and warm acidified potassium permanganate, (b) iodine in potassium iodide.

Preparation and analysis of potassium nitrilosulphonate, $N(SO_3K)_3 \cdot 2 H_2O$

The reaction of urea with very strong sulphuric acid produces, according to the conditions, amidosulphuric acid, $NH_2 \cdot SO_3H$, and imidosulphuric acid, $NH(SO_3H)_2$. A third compound, nitrilosulphonic acid, $N(SO_3H)_3$, can be prepared by a slightly different route. These acids can be regarded as sulphonic derivatives of ammonia. Prepare $N(SO_3K)_3 \cdot 2 H_2O$ by the reaction

$$KNO_2 + 4 KHSO_3 \rightarrow N(SO_3K)_3 + K_2SO_3 + 2 H_2O$$

Procedure

Dissolve 20 g. potassium metabisulphite in 25–30 ml. nearly boiling water in a beaker. Put a solution of 2·5 g. potassium nitrite in 10 ml. cold water in a burette. Adjust the bisulphite solution to 50–60°c and add, stirring continuously, the nitrite solution. The temperature rises spontaneously to nearly 100°c during mixing and crystals soon form in the liquid. Add a few millilitres of concentrated ammonium hydroxide to the mixture to make it strongly alkaline and then leave it undisturbed for one hour.

Transfer the liquid and crystals to a 250 ml. flask, washing out the beaker into the flask with 50 ml. hot water. Add another 100 ml. hot water, a few millilitres of concentrated ammonium hydroxide, and then redissolve all the solid by heating. Cool the solution rapidly by running cold water over the flask and stimulate the formation of *small* crystals by shaking and stirring the liquid. Filter by suction and wash twice on the filter with ice-cold dilute ammonium hydroxide.

Transfer the solid to a beaker containing 50 ml. ice-cold dilute ammonium hydroxide and thoroughly mix the crystals with the liquid. Filter and test a portion of filtrate, after acidification, with dilute potassium permanganate. If decolourization occurs, wash on the filter with more ice-cold dilute aqueous ammonia until all traces of sulphite are removed. Then wash with ethanol and finally with acetone. Dry at room temperature.

Analysis

Heat samples of approximately 0·5 g. on a boiling water bath with a mixture of 20 ml. water and 10 ml. N/10 hydrochloric acid for half an hour. After cooling, titrate with standardized, approximately N/10 sodium hydroxide.

Preparation of potassium cyanate, KNCO*

Grind together in a dry mortar 8 g. urea crystals and 10 g. potassium bicarbonate. Transfer the mixture to a porcelain basin in a fume cupboard and heat very gently until fusion occurs and gases cease to evolve.

Test the melt for absence of carbonate as follows. Remove a drop on the end of a dry glass rod, allow it to solidify and then dissolve it in 2–3 ml. water. Add barium chloride solution; if no precipitate forms within a few minutes, carbonate is absent from the melt. Should carbonate prove to be present, a further small amount of urea (0·5 g.) should be added to the melt and heated.

When no carbonate is left, remove the basin from the source of heat and swirl the melt round the basin as it cools. Powder the crude cyanate in the mortar and mix in a beaker with 10 ml. water. Add a few drops of potassium hydroxide to make it alkaline and heat the whole to 50°c with stirring. When only a small amount of solid remains undissolved, quickly filter the solution on a Buchner funnel with suction. Transfer the filtrate to a beaker and warm gently if any crystals form on cooling. Add 25 ml. ethanol and cool the mixture in ice. Filter the separated crystals on a Buchner funnel, wash with ethanol and ether and dry *in vacuo*. Record the yield of product.

Exercises

1. To an aqueous solution add dilute acid. What gas is evolved?
2. To the above reaction solution add excess sodium hydroxide and warm. What gas is evolved?
3. Deduce the equation for the hydrolysis of potassium cyanate as follows:

Dissolve about 0·5 g. (accurately weighed) of pure potassium cyanate in 10 ml. water in a conical flask. Add 50 ml. N hydrochloric acid whereupon effervescence occurs. Boil the solution for 20 min. to complete hydrolysis. Cool the liquid and titrate with N sodium hydroxide using methyl orange as indicator. From this titre the total acid used in the hydrolysis can be calculated.

Ammonia is also liberated and during the course of the reaction is instantly neutralized by the acid, so that the above titre includes that due to the ammonia neutralization. To determine the amount of ammonia produced add the following solution. To 5 ml. formaldehyde solution (formalin) add a few drops of phenolphthalein and then add sodium hydroxide dropwise until exactly neutral. Now titrate the whole of this with alkali until the colour of phenolphthalein develops. The formaldehyde reacts with ammonium ion liberating H^+.

$$6 \ HCHO + 4 \ NH_4^+ \rightarrow 4 \ H^+ + (CH_2)_6N_4 + 6 \ H_2O$$

It is this H^+ that is now being determined which is equivalent to the ammonia produced.

* Adapted from Palmer, *Experimental Inorganic Chemistry*.

Deductions. The ratio of the total acid used in hydrolysis (1st titration) to the acid used to react with ammonia (2nd titration) is $x:y$. What is your ratio? Simplify this ratio to something of the form $1:2$, $3:1$, $4:1$. The equation can be partially formulated:

$$z \text{ NCO}^- + (x - y) \text{ H}^+ + \text{H}_2\text{O} \rightarrow y \text{ NH}_3$$

We know x and y but not z. The weight of potassium cyanate taken is known. Calculate the weight of NH_3 produced from the second titration figure. From these weights, work out the molecular ratio $\text{KNCO}:\text{NH}_3$. This equals $z:y$. Complete the equation from the data above and check that it is balanced.

$$z \text{ NCO}^- + (x - y) \text{ H}^+ + \text{H}_2\text{O} \rightarrow y \text{ NH}_3 + \text{X (gas)}$$

Preparation of orthoarsenates, M_3AsO_4

1. *Orthoarsenic acid, H_3AsO_4*

SAFETY NOTE   Carry out this experiment in a fume cupboard.

Add slowly, from a dropping funnel, 10 ml. concentrated nitric acid to 10 g. arsenious oxide in a round-bottom flask. Heat the mixture gently until evolution of nitrogen oxides ceases, decant the supernatant liquid from undissolved material and evaporate the solution to dryness. Dissolve the residue in the minimum of water, filter, if necessary, on a sintered glass filter, and evaporate the solution until its temperature reaches 130°c. Remove a portion for the next experiment and leave the remaining syrupy liquid to crystallize in a refrigerator (in a desiccator over concentrated sulphuric acid).

2. *Ammonium orthoarsenate, $(NH_4)_3AsO_4 \cdot 3 H_2O$*

To the portion of orthoarsenic acid removed from the previous experiment, add concentrated ammonium hydroxide, or preferably, bubble ammonia gas through the solution. Filter the white crystals formed and dry on a porous plate. Ampoule.

Analysis

Analyse your products for arsenic after reduction with excess potassium iodide.

Reference

Brauer, *Handbook of Preparative Inorganic Chemistry*, Vol. 1, p. 602.

Cationic chemistry of antimony

The sulphate is one of the few ionic salts formed by antimony. Even this readily hydrolyses to $(\text{SbO})_2\text{SO}_4$. Compare this behaviour with that of bismuth which forms several ionic salts, e.g., $Bi(NO_3)_3$, $BiPO_4$, $BiBO_3$, showing the increase in electropositive behaviour down the group.

1. *Antimony(III) sulphate, $Sb_2(SO_4)_3$*

Dissolve 10 g. antimonous oxide, Sb_2O_3, in 50 ml. hot concentrated sulphuric acid and, when dissolved, allow to cool. Wash the crystals free from sulphuric acid with excess xylene followed by ether.

2. *Antimony oxysulphate, $(SbO)_2SO_4$*

Hydrolyse a portion of antimony sulphate in excess cold water. Filter and dry at 100°c.

Analysis

Analyse your products for antimony using Andrew's titration (potassium iodate and concentrated hydrochloric acid).

4.6 Group VI

Reactions of group VI elements

1. *Oxides.* Prepare samples of tellurium dioxide and selenium dioxide by oxidizing small portions of selenium and tellurium with concentrated nitric acid in a small crucible. Evaporate just to dryness, cool, add a little water and again take to dryness. Correlate the state of the oxides O_3, SO_2, SeO_2 and TeO_2 with their structures and compare their reactivities towards water. What products are formed?

2. *Oxyanions, MO_3^{2-},* sulphite, selenite and tellurite. Test each for (a) oxidizing action with potassium iodide solution and sulphur dioxide, (b) reducing action with iodine solution.

3. *Oxyanions, MO_4^{2-},* sulphate, selenate and tellurate. Test each for the ability to oxidize salts of hydroxylamine and hydrazine.

Put the oxyanions MO_3^{2-} and MO_4^{2-} in order of increasing oxidizing strength.

Preparation of disulphur dichloride, S_2Cl_2

SAFETY NOTE   Use a fume cupboard.

Reflux a mixture of 4 g. sulphur and 8 g. sulphuryl chloride, SO_2Cl_2, together with a speck of aluminium chloride as catalyst in a

50 ml. flask for 20 min. using a water bath at 70°c. Reassemble the semi-micro apparatus, figure 4.2, and distil the disulphur dichloride. Collect the orange-red liquid, b.p. 138°c, in a 25 ml. flask. Ampoule that portion of product which is not used for the following tests.

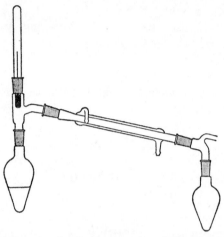

Figure 4.2. Apparatus for the preparation of disulphur dichloride.

Exercises

1. Add one drop of disulphur dichloride to a test-tube containing water. What are the products of hydrolysis?
2. Devise a method for analysis of your compound and determine its purity.
3. Test the solvent properties of disulphur dichloride for sulphur.

Preparation of telluric acid, H_6TeO_6

To 100 ml. water, add 40 ml. concentrated nitric acid and 10 g. tellurium dioxide. Boil the suspension and add in 5 ml. portions at 5 min. intervals a solution of 5 g. potassium permanganate in 100 ml. water. Remove the manganese dioxide produced by slowly adding hydrogen peroxide to the hot solution (about 50 ml. is sufficient). Evaporate the solution to 50 ml. and add 10 ml. concentrated nitric acid; leave to crystallize overnight. Cool in ice and filter. Wash the crystals with concentrated nitric acid, then with ice-cold water, and recrystallize from the minimum of hot water.

Exercises

1. Analyse your product by titrating a solution with sodium hydroxide, using phenolphthalein as indicator. Add a volume of glycerol equal to that of the

telluric acid solution taken; the glycerol enhances the acidity of the telluric acid. H_6TeO_6 is a monobasic acid.

2. Compare the structure and properties of sulphuric and telluric acids. Compare the reaction of the two acids towards (a) barium chloride solution and (b) warm concentrated hydrochloric acid.

Reference

F. C. Mathers *et. al.*, *Inorg. Synth.*, **3**, 145.

4.7 Group VII

Reactions of the halogens

The properties of these elements should be well known. The following experiments illustrate trends in the group and some less common properties. Use sodium or potassium salts.

1. Add concentrated sulphuric acid to each halide. Test for gases liberated (in the case of fluoride, warm).

2. Add chlorine water to solutions of each halide.

3. Add bromine water to solutions of each halide.

4. Using not more than one pin-head of salts of the oxyanions chlorate, bromate and iodate, investigate their reaction with concentrated sulphuric acid in an ignition tube.

5. Pass chlorine into a tube containing 0·5 g. iodine. Observe carefully the course of the reaction and comment on the nature of the products.

6. Compare qualitatively the solubility of iodine in (a) water, (b) potassium iodide solution and (c) concentrated hydrochloric acid. Investigate as far as you are able the extraction of iodine from each solution into carbon tetrachloride or chloroform.

Correlate the above reactions with trends within the group.

Preparation of potassium metaperiodate, KIO_4*

Add 8 g. potassium peroxodisulphate to a boiling solution of 5 g. potassium iodate and 5g. potassium hydroxide in 50 ml. water. Stir and add 3 g. potassium hydroxide one pellet at a time. Heat for 20 min. on a water bath, add 50 ml. water and cool the solution. Filter if necessary and cool in ice. Add from a burette 1:1 nitric acid with stirring until acid to methyl orange. Then add 1 ml. of the acid in excess. Filter the white product, wash with water and dry in air.

---

* Adapted from Palmer, *Experimental Inorganic Chemistry*.

Exercises

1. Analysis. Dissolve 0·1 g. potassium metaperiodate in 100 ml. water and add 2 g. borax, excess boric acid and 3 g. potassium iodide. Allow the mixture to stand for 3 min. and titrate the liberated iodine with sodium thiosulphate. After titration, acidify with excess hydrochloric acid and continue the titration.

    (a) What is the ratio of your titration figures?

    (b) What were the stages in the reduction?

2. Boil a mixture of potassium iodate, sodium hydroxide and copper sulphate, and add potassium peroxodisulphate slowly. What is formed in solution?

3. The iodate ion, IO_3^-, and xenon trioxide, XeO_3, are isoelectronic. What are their structures? What governs their stereochemistry and why are they stable?

Chapter 5

Transition Metal Chemistry:
Reactions and Preparations

This chapter contains a series of tests designed to illustrate the chemistry of the first-row transition elements. Performed and answered conscientiously, they also form a useful revision of some aspects of the theory of transition metal ions. You will probably wish to extend or alter these tests: consult the demonstrator before doing so.

Preparations follow the tests and together they cover a fair variety of complexes and most types of stereochemistry. They can mostly be performed within one or two laboratory periods (three hours).

For each preparation, record the weights of starting materials, the yield and percentage yield obtained. Label your products with your name, the formula of the compounds and the weight of material.

5.1 Titanium

Reactions of titanium

Use a solution of titanic sulphate or chloride.

Record all observations and interpret them as far as possible.

1. Examine the effect of concentrated sodium hydroxide and ammonium hydroxide. Warm gently.

2. Add dilute sulphuric acid followed by a few drops of hydrogen peroxide solution. Observe the results and then add excess ammonium fluoride.

3. Take 10 ml. of solution, add dilute sulphuric acid and granulated zinc. Observe the changes that take place. Decant the solution from the zinc and use it for the following tests.

(a) Add excess ammonium hydroxide.
(b) Add excess sodium hydroxide and heat gently.
(c) Add a few drops of hydrogen peroxide solution.
(d) Add dilute potassium permanganate solution dropwise.
(e) Record or refer to the visible spectrum of the solution. Comment upon (i) the number of bands, (ii) the band width, (iii) the band symmetry, and (iv) the extinction coefficient.

Preparation of titanium complexes

1. *Adduct with phosphorus oxychloride,* $(TiCl_4 \cdot POCl_3)_2$

Since titanium tetrachloride is a strong Lewis acid, it readily forms addition compounds of the type $R_2O \cdot TiCl_4$ and $(R_2O)_2 \cdot TiCl_4$ with oxygen donors such as ethers, alcohols, etc.

Mix together equimolar solutions of titanium tetrachloride and phosphorus oxychloride, each in carbon tetrachloride. Filter off the yellow adduct and recrystallize from chloroform. Remove occluded solvent under reduced pressure.

2. *Complex with acetylacetone, cis—$[Ti(acac)_2Cl_2]$*

To 10 ml. glacial acetic acid, add 1 ml. acetic anhydride and 3·2 ml. titanium tetrachloride. Cool in ice and add 6 ml. acetylacetone. Boil (in a fume cupboard) and, on cooling, a red-yellow crystalline precipitate forms. Decant the mother liquor, wash the crystals with petroleum ether (b.p. 60–80°c) and vacuum dry in a desiccator. Recrystallize from boiling glacial acetic acid–acetic anhydride mixture (12 : 1).

Reactions

Mix together solutions of anhydrous ferric chloride and the acetylacetone complex in glacial acetic acid and isolate the red crystalline complex produced. What is its composition?

Questions

1. What are the structures of the above titanium complexes?
2. How do these compounds behave towards water? Test the solution for halide ions – does this suggest a method for analysis? Carry out an analysis for one element on one of your compounds.
3. Compare the coordination chemistries of titanium and silicon.

References

1. D. S. Payne, *Rec. Trav. chim.*, 1956, **75**, 620.
2. R. C. Young and A. J. Van der Weyden, *Inorg. Synth.*, **2**, 119.
3. I. R. Beattie, *Quart. Rev.*, 1963, **17**, 382.

5.2 Vanadium

Reactions of vanadium

Suspend about 0·5 g. ammonium metavanadate, NH_4VO_3, in 5 ml. water and add 5 ml. dilute sodium hydroxide. Dilute to 25 ml. and use this solution for tests 1–5. Record all observations and interpret them as far as possible.

1. Slowly acidify with (a) dilute hydrochloric acid, (b) dilute sulphuric acid. What is the effect of adding excess acid?
2. Acidify with dilute sulphuric acid and pass hydrogen sulphide.
3. Pass sulphur dioxide through the solution.
4. Acidify with dilute hydrochloric acid and add a piece of granulated zinc or zinc amalgam. Observe the changes which take place over 30 min.
5. Acidify with dilute sulphuric acid and add hydrogen peroxide dropwise. Then add ammonium fluoride in excess.
6. Using *solid* ammonium metavanadate
(a) Add concentrated hydrochloric acid to a small amount and note what happens on gentle warming. What compound is formed?
(b) Strongly heat a small sample. What compound is produced? Dissolve some of the compound formed in concentrated hydrochloric acid and comment on any reaction.

Preparation of vanadyl acetylacetonate, $[VO(acac)_2]$

Boil a solution of 5 g. vanadium pentoxide in 12 ml. water to which has been added 9 ml. concentrated sulphuric acid and 25 ml. ethanol. Reflux for 1–2 hr., the colour of the slurry changes to blue-green. Filter and add 13 ml. acetylacetone to the solution. Neutralize the solution by adding slowly and with stirring a solution of 20 g. anhydrous sodium carbonate in 125 ml. water. Filter the product and dry in air. Recrystallize from chloroform.

Adduct with pyridine

Reflux equimolar quantities of vanadyl acetylacetonate and pyridine in ether. Filter and evaporate the ether from the filtrate (fume cupboard, steam bath).

Exercises

1. What are the structures of vanadyl acetylacetonate and the pyridine adduct?
2. Would you expect an adduct to form with triphenylphosphine?
3. The V=O stretching frequency of $[VO(acac)_2]$ is 995 cm.$^{-1}$ and this is shifted to 964 cm.$^{-1}$ in the pyridine adduct. Can you explain this?

References

1. R. A. Rowe and M. M. Jones, *Inorg. Synth.*, **5**, 114.
2. M. M. Jones, *J. Amer. Chem. Soc.*, 1954, **76**, 5995.

5.3 Chromium and Molybdenum

Reactions of chromium

Record all observations and interpret them as far as possible.
For the following tests, use potassium dichromate.

1. Add a drop of sodium hydroxide to a solution of potassium dichromate.

2. Add a few drops of concentrated sulphuric acid to solid potassium dichromate. Notice the colour change. Add solid sodium chloride and warm gently.

3. Add hydrogen peroxide dropwise to a solution of potassium dichromate to which has been added an equal volume of ether. What occurs on shaking? Repeat this test using an alkaline solution.

4. Warm a mixture of 1 g. potassium dichromate in 1 ml. concentrated hydrochloric acid and 1 ml. water. Allow to stand, and recrystallize the product from acetone.

5. Dissolve in dilute hydrochloric acid and add formaldehyde. Cool and add granulated zinc.

For the following tests use chrome alum solution.

1) Reduce with zinc and hydrochloric acid.

2) Add ammonium or potassium peroxodisulphate and one drop of silver nitrate solution and warm.

Preparation of pyridine perchromate [$CrO_5 \cdot C_5H_5N$]

Dissolve 4 g. chromium trioxide in 150 ml. water and add 9 ml. pyridine. Cool in an ice–salt mixture and add 4 ml. 30% hydrogen peroxide in 20 ml. water. Filter the blue needles, wash with water and pump dry in air.

SAFETY NOTE   Old samples of this substance have been known to explode. Destroy *all* material with dilute alkali before leaving the laboratory.

Exercises

1. Test for solubility in ether and water.
2. Observe the effect of adding dilute sulphuric acid.
3. Add a little of the complex to neutral potassium permanganate solution (approx. N/100). Explain the result.
4. Draw the structure of the complex. How is the peroxy group bonded to the chromium?

References

1. K. A. Hofmann and H. Heindlmaier, *Ber.*, 1905, **38**, 3066.
2. D. G. Tuck and R. M. Walters, *Inorg. Chem.*, 1963, **2**, 428.
3. J. A. Connor and E. A. V. Ebsworth, *Adv. Inorg. Chem. Radiochem.*, 1964, **6**, 303.

Preparation of potassium octacyanomolybdate (IV), $K_4[Mo(CN)_8] \cdot 2 H_2O$

Dissolve 8·5 g. molybdic acid in 75 ml. 1 : 1 hydrochloric acid and heat on a steam bath. Add slowly and with constant stirring a solution of 19 g. potassium thiocyanate in 40 ml. water. Heat the resulting red solution for 2 hr. and then filter. Transfer the filtrate to a 250 ml. beaker and add slowly with stirring 4–5 ml. pyridine until a yellow solid just begins to separate. Place the beaker in an ice bath until the red oily layer which separates out at the bottom becomes very viscous. Decant the supernatant liquid and wash the product twice with water. Treat the oily liquid with a solution of 12·5 g. potassium cyanide in 40 ml. water *in a fume cupboard* and heat on a steam bath for half an hour with frequent stirring. If any black by-product separates out, remove by filtration. Concentrate the solution to half bulk and cool in ice. Collect the crystals formed on a Buchner funnel.

Dissolve the crude product in the minimum quantity of water at 70°C, treat with decolourizing charcoal and filter. Add to the filtrate 1–2 volumes of ethyl alcohol until a yellow solid separates. Collect the powder on a Buchner funnel, wash with alcohol, then ether and finally dry in a vacuum desiccator. The bright yellow product can be recrystallized if necessary from water. Solutions are photosensitive and may yield a green product if stood in light.

Exercises

1. Determine the purity of the compound by oxidation with ceric sulphate in dilute sulphuric acid, using ferroin as indicator.
2. Draw the structure of the octacyanomolybdate anion.
3. List some other 8-coordinate complexes and draw their structures.

References

1. L. F. Fieser, *J. Amer. Chem. Soc.*, 1930, **52**, 5226.
2. L. E. Orgel, *J. Inorg. Nuclear Chem.*, 1960, **14**, 136.
3. N. H. Furman and C. O. Miller, *Inorg. Synth.*, **3**, 160.

5.4 Manganese

Reactions of manganese

Use a solution of manganous chloride or sulphate for tests 1, 2, 3 and 5. Record all observations and interpret them as far as possible.
1. Add sodium hydroxide solution.
2. Add 1 ml. sodium hydroxide and 1 ml. hydrogen peroxide. Filter, wash the precipitate and heat it with dilute hydrochloric acid. Test for chlorine evolution.
3. Add 1 ml. dilute nitric acid and heat. Add sodium bismuthate.
4. Using solid potassium permanganate
(a) Add to very strong sodium hydroxide and boil. Cool the solution and acidify.

(b) Add *one pin-head only* of powdered solid to *cold* concentrated sulphuric acid in an ignition tube.

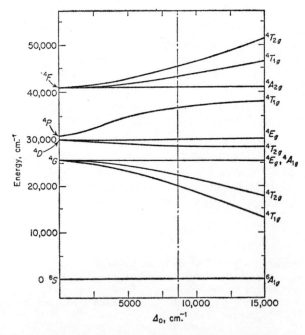

Figure 5.1. Partial energy level diagram for d^5 ion in an octahedral environment. For $[Mn(H_2O)_6]^{2+}$, $\Delta_0 = 8600$ cm.$^{-1}$. (Reproduced from F. A. Cotton and G. Wilkinson, *Advanced Inorganic Chemistry*, Interscience, New York, 1962, p. 702.)

5. Record or refer to the UV visible spectrum of manganese(II) in water.

(a) How many bands and shoulders are there?

(b) Comment upon the extinction coefficients of the bands.

(c) Assign the transitions with reference to the energy-level diagram, figure 5.1.

(d) Why are some bands broad and others narrow?

Preparation of potassium hexacyanomanganate(III), $K_3[Mn(CN)_6]$

Dissolve 25 g. potassium cyanide in the minimum quantity of water (~ 50 ml.) in a 250 ml. conical flask. Add 6·5 g. manganese carbonate in small portions, crushing any lumps that form. Oxidize the blue compound formed, $K_4[Mn(CN)_6]$, by warming on a hot-plate at 70°C and drawing air through it for several hours until all the solid has turned brown. Cool the flask in ice, filter and wash the solid with alcohol. Add 0·5 g. potassium cyanide to the solid and dissolve most of the combined solids in the minimum of water. Filter any residue and reduce to half bulk in a desiccator containing phosphorus pentoxide to obtain red crystals of the hexacyano-manganate(III).

Exercises

1. Analyse the complex after hydrolysis in boiling water. Filter the precipitated manganic hydroxide, add potassium iodide and concentrated hydrochloric acid and titrate with potassium iodate (Andrews' titration).

2. In a determination of the magnetic moment of this compound, the susceptibility, χ, was found to be $12·65 \times 10^{-6}$ cm.^{3} g.$^{-1}$ at 20°C. Calculate the magnetic moment in Bohr Magnetons. What can you deduce from this figure? (See Chapter 16.)

Reference

F. A. Cotton et. al., J. Inorg. Nuclear Chem., 1959, **10**, 28.

5.5 Iron

Reactions of iron

Record all observations and interpret them as far as possible.

1. Investigate the effects of adding (a) sodium hydroxide and (b) ammonium hydroxide to a solution containing iron(II). Do the precipitates dissolve in excess reagent? To each, add hydrogen peroxide.

2. Add potassium thiocyanate solution to a solution containing iron(III). Divide the solution into two parts:
(a) add a little ammonium fluoride,
(b) add stannous chloride.
3. Add citric acid to a solution containing iron(III). Make alkaline with ammonia.

Preparation of potassium tris(oxalato)ferrate(III), $K_3[Fe(C_2O_4)_3] \cdot 3 H_2O$*

To a well stirred solution of 5 g. ferrous ammonium sulphate in 20 ml. warm water containing 1 ml. dilute sulphuric acid, add 2·5 g. oxalic acid dihydrate in 25 ml. water. Heat the solution very slowly to boiling and allow the yellow precipitate of ferrous oxalate to settle. Decant the supernatant liquid, add a further 15 ml. hot water to the solid, stir and filter. Transfer the ferrous oxalate so prepared to a beaker and add 3·5 g. potassium oxalate monohydrate in 10 ml. warm water. Add slowly from a burette 8 ml. ' 20 volume' hydrogen peroxide, stirring the liquid continuously and keeping the temperature near 40°c. Heat the solution to boiling and dissolve precipitated ferric hydroxide by adding 20 ml. of a solution of oxalic acid containing 1 g. in 30 ml. water. Add further oxalic acid solution dropwise from a burette until all the ferric hydroxide has dissolved. During this addition, keep the solution nearly boiling. Filter the hot solution and add 30 ml. ethanol to the filtrate. Redissolve any crystals formed by gentle heating and set aside the solution in a dark cupboard overnight for crystallization. Filter and wash the crystals with a 1:1 ethanol:water mixture and finally with acetone. The complex is photosensitive and the surface of the crystals will soon become coated with yellow ferrous oxalate unless stored in the dark.

Exercises

1. Calculate the paramagnetic moment of the complex. Compare your value with a literature value.
2. Analyse the complex for oxalate.
3. How many isomers does the complex have?

Preparation of nitrosylbis(diethyldithiocarbamato)iron(I), $[Fe(NO)(S_2CNEt_2)_2]$

Dissolve approximately 5 g. ferrous sulphate and 1·5 g. sodium nitrite in 25 ml. dilute sulphuric acid, using a fume cupboard. Immediately

* Adapted from Palmer, *Experimental Inorganic Chemistry*.

add 10 g. sodium diethyldithiocarbamate and stir vigorously for 5 min. Extract the dark-coloured compound in chloroform from which it crystallizes on evaporation.

Exercises

1. What is the structure of the compound? How is the nitric oxide group bonded to the iron?
2. The N—O stretching frequency in nitric oxide is 1878 cm.$^{-1}$. Why is the frequency shifted to about 1626 cm.$^{-1}$ when NO is bonded in this complex?

References

1. L. Cambi and A. Cagnasso, *Chem. Abs.*, 1932, **26**, 41.
2. P. R. H. Alderman, P. G. Owston and J. M. Rowe, *J. Chem. Soc.*, 1962, 668

5.6 Cobalt

Reactions of cobalt

Use a solution of cobalt chloride or nitrate.

Record all observations and interpret them as far as possible.

1. Add sodium hydroxide. Does the precipitate dissolve in excess? Add hydrogen peroxide.

2. Repeat test 1 using ammonium hydroxide.

3. Add ammonium thiocyanate solution followed by a little acetone and divide into three parts:

(a) shake with ether,

(b) add a mercuric nitrate (or chloride) solution and boil,

(c) add ammonium fluoride.

4. Add potassium nitrite solution and acidify with dilute acetic solution.

5. Add potassium cyanide solution and bubble air through the solution.

6. Add sodium chloride and warm.

7. Record the visible spectrum of an aqueous solution of cobalt chloride or nitrate and of the solution obtained in test 3.

Account for (a) the colours of the solutions and (b) the extinction coefficients of the bands.

Preparation of mercury tetrathiocyanatocobalt(II), Hg[Co(SCN)$_4$]

Add with stirring a boiling solution of 14 g. cobalt sulphate heptahydrate and 15 g. ammonium thiocyanate in 25 ml. water to a boiling filtered solution of 13·5 g. mercuric chloride in 150 ml. water.

Boil and stir vigorously for 2 min. Wash by decantation and dry at 120°c.

Exercises

1 What is the structure of the complex?

2. In a determination of the magnetic moment of this compound, the susceptibility, χ, was found to be $16·44 \times 10^{-6}$ cm.^{3} g.$^{-1}$ at 20°c. Calculate the magnetic moment in Bohr Magnetons. What can you deduce from this figure? (See Chapter 16.)

Reference

B. N. Figgis and R. S. Nyholm, *J. Chem. Soc.*, 1958, 4190.

5.7 Nickel

Reactions of nickel

Use a solution of nickel sulphate or chloride.

Record all observations and interpret them as far as possible.

1. Examine the effect of sodium hydroxide and ammonium hydroxide.

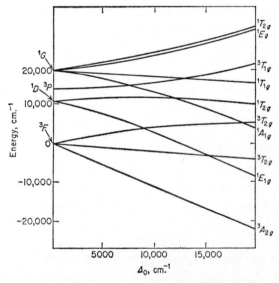

Figure 5.2. Partial energy level diagram for d^8 ion (Ni^{2+}) in an octahedral environment. The ^1S state at high energy is omitted. (Reproduced, by permission, from L. E. Orgel, *J. Chem. Phys.*, 1955, **23**, 1009.)

2. Investigate the effect of dimethylglyoxime at different pH. Do cobaltous solutions give a precipitate under similar conditions?

3. Add potassium cyanide solution dropwise and divide the solution into two parts:
   (a) add sodium hydroxide solution,
   (b) crystallize and isolate any solid formed.

4. Record the visible and ultraviolet spectrum of a solution of nickel chloride in water. Now add ethylenediamine hydrate to the solution and repeat the spectrum.
   (a) How many bands are there in each spectrum?
   (b) Assign the transitions with reference to the energy-level diagram (figure 5.2).
   (c) Why is the spectrum shifted to higher frequencies when ethylenediamine is added?

Preparation of potassium trifluoronickelate, $KNiF_3$

Boil a solution of 3·5 g. potassium fluoride in water and add a few drops of dilute nitric acid. Add with stirring a solution of 4·8 g. hydrated nickel chloride. Maintain the temperature of the resulting solution near boiling for 15 min. Filter, and wash the precipitate well with cold water followed by alcohol. Dry the yellow product at 100°c.

Exercises

1. Analyse gravimetrically for fluoride by converting the compound to lead chloride fluoride.
2. Draw the crystal structure of the complex. How many fluoride nearest neighbours has each nickel and each potassium atom?

Investigation of the clathrate behaviour of dicyanoammine-nickel(II), $[Ni(CN)_2 \cdot NH_3 \cdot X]$

The ability of ammoniacal nickel cyanide solutions to take up certain organic molecules, X, to form a clathrate of the general formula $[Ni(CN)_2 \cdot NH_3 \cdot X]$ is dependent on the size and shape of the organic molecule. This is illustrated in this experiment, where it is shown that only one component of an m-cresol-aniline mixture is taken up.

Procedure

Add a solution of 7 g. potassium cyanide in 50 ml. water to 12 g. hydrated nickel chloride in 50 ml. water. Add 56 ml. concentrated ammonium hydroxide and cool in ice. Filter any residue and add

60% acetic acid slowly until a turbidity appears. Now add a mixture of 5 ml. *m*-cresol and 5 ml. aniline and shake for 1 hr., followed by cooling in ice. Filter the solid complex, wash with water, alcohol and ether and dry in air. Using a semimicro distillation apparatus, carefully dry distil the complex and collect the organic distillate, noting its boiling point. Test the distillate for presence of aniline by diazotization and coupling with β-naphthol; test for *m*-cresol with ferric chloride solution.

Questions

1. Which organic compound is taken up in preference? Why?
2. Draw the structure of the complex. Calculate its magnetic moment.

Reference

R. F. Evans *et. al.*, *J. Chem. Soc.*, 1950, 3346.

5.8 Copper

Reactions of copper

Use a cupric sulphate solution except in (6) and (7).

Record all observations and interpret them as far as possible.

1. Add a solution of potassium cyanide, followed by excess of the reagent.

2. Add sodium hydroxide and boil.

3. Add sodium hydroxide followed by sodium hypochlorite. Acidify, and identify the gas liberated.

4. Add a piece of zinc.

5. Add sodium hydroxide, potassium iodate and potassium peroxodisulphate and boil. Acidify, and identify the gas liberated.

6. Add granulated or powdered copper metal to a concentrated solution of potassium cyanide and warm. Identify the gas liberated.

7. Heat solid copper sulphate pentahydrate. Why is there a colour change?

8. Record the visible spectrum of (a) a solution of copper(II) sulphate and (b) a solution of copper(II) sulphate to which has been added excess ammonium hydroxide. Comment on (i) the number of bands, (ii) the band width, (iii) the band symmetry, (iv) the extinction coefficients and (v) the relative positions of ε_{max}.

Section II

Advanced Preparative and Structural Techniques

The object of the experiments in this section is to introduce you to a selection of the more important preparative and structural techniques used in modern inorganic chemistry. Some experiments are mainly of a preparative nature, in others the emphasis is upon a physical technique, but very few are solely preparative or structural. This close conjunction of preparative and structural methods is a feature of modern chemical research. For example, infrared spectroscopy is routinely used by nearly all preparative chemists; many of the following experiments require you to record an infrared spectrum.

Exercises and questions are appended to most experiments. These are not merely 'riders', the solution of which will gain you credit. They are intended to prompt thought about the experiment or a particular product, to lead you to study selected portions of the literature, and above all to stimulate curiosity. Several of the experiments in this book have developed from discussions in the laboratory or from a student extending or improving a given exercise.

In a final-year honours practical course in inorganic chemistry of about 90–100 hours, you will probably complete eight to twelve of these experiments. These should be selected to cover as wide a range of techniques and chemical 'types' as possible. As, in general, there will be many more experiments running than you will be able to do, take a part-time interest in some of the other experiments if you can do this without disturbing the persons concerned.

Before you attempt this part of the course, you should study carefully Appendix 1 which deals with 'Safety in the Laboratory'.

Some experiments in which the primary aim is the use of a physical technique require several compounds: it is not the best use of your limited time in the laboratory to perform all these preparations if the compounds are already available. When a course such as this has run for a year or more there will be a stock of such chemicals ready for your use. If this is not the case, work in pairs for experiments requiring a lot of preparation or share the results of one preparation amongst several people. The object of this course is to enable you to see and carry out and learn as much chemistry as possible.

The first chapter of this section deals with infrared spectroscopy as this technique is required in connection with many of the other experiments.

Chapter 6

Infrared Spectroscopy

One of the most characteristic properties of a polynuclear molecule is its infrared spectrum. For a gas, this is its vibration–rotation (or, at low frequencies, pure rotation) spectrum. For condensed phases, the infrared spectrum is effectively the vibrational spectrum, the maximum number of infrared active frequencies possible being $(3N - 6)$ for a non-linear molecule of N atoms. Only those vibrational distortions of the molecule which give rise to a change of dipole moment interact with infrared radiation. The Raman spectrum is equally important and informative but commercial instrumentation in this field is neither as plentiful nor as well developed, and, indeed, is useless for materials which are strongly coloured. The activity of Raman scattering is determined by changes in the polarizability tensor. If the molecule has a centre of symmetry there will be no coincidences between the infrared and Raman spectra – the mutual exclusion rule. In most other cases some vibrational modes, at least, will be coincident in frequency in both types of spectrum.

We have used the term 'vibrational mode' because it implies that a vibration is a property of the molecule *as a whole*, and is not necessarily localized. This is important and it is essential to understand the implications for inorganic spectroscopy. For purposes of description and calculation, the motions of the constituent atoms of a molecule during a vibration may be referred to a set of coordinates known as 'internal coordinates'. Often, these are bond lengths and angles. For example, for the water molecule, the two O—H bond lengths and the H—O—H angle would be used. For any given vibrational mode there will be *some* change in *all* of these coordinates, although it may well happen that most of the distortion occurs in one or more of them. The distribution of kinetic energy amongst the internal coordinates can be calculated, given the geometry of the molecule and the observed vibrational frequencies. If it is found that most of the kinetic energy of a given vibration is associated with a limited set of bonds and inter-bond angles then it is reasonable to refer to it as a vibration of that set of bonds and angles. This is the basis of the concept of 'group frequencies'. Clearly, it is an approximate description, although sometimes a very good one; indeed without it the chemical application of molecular spectroscopy would probably still be in its infancy. But the very fact that all group frequencies occur within a *range* of frequencies indicates that there is some interaction between the vibrations of that group and the rest of the molecule. There is no hard and fast rule as to where the line should be drawn between what is a group frequency and what is not.

Organic chemistry deals with a severely restricted set of atoms and bond types: it is therefore not surprising that frequencies associated with certain molecular groups (e.g., methyl, ethylenic double bonds, etc.) remain roughly constant throughout a wide variety of organic molecular types. The inorganic chemist deals with about a hundred different atoms, and a very wide range of bond types, so it is essential for him to treat the concept of group frequencies with reserve. There are many known instances in which a given vibration can only be regarded as being of the whole molecule. This situation is particularly likely for metal–ligand bond vibrations. For example, a recent calculation (I. R. Beattie and T. Gilson)[*] for the molecule [AlH$_3$(NMe$_3$)$_2$], which has the trigonal bipyramid form with N—Al—N linear, shows that in one particular antisymmetric vibration the kinetic energy is distributed in roughly equal proportions between Al—N bond stretching, NC$_3$ bond stretching and NC$_3$ deformation. There is, thus, no such thing as an N—Al—N antisymmetric stretch in this molecule.

Most of the spectroscopy with which you will be concerned in this course can still profitably use the group frequency concept (e.g. the internal vibrations of —NH$_3$ or —NO$_2$ groups when coordinated to metals). In more complex systems the above cautions will apply.

The only comprehensive reference book available in the inorganic field at the moment is by K. Nakamoto, *Infrared Spectra of Inorganic and Coordination Compounds*, Wiley, New York, 1963. A good introduction to Raman spectroscopy in inorganic chemistry is given by L. A. Woodward in *Quart. Rev.*, 1956, **10**, 185.

Instrumentation

Several low-cost infrared spectrophotometers are now on the market. They are designed for use 'at the bench' and mostly have only three

J. Chem. Soc., **1964**, 3528.

or four controls. We shall not attempt a detailed description of any one instrument: see the manufacturers' instructions.

In general these instruments cover 2–15 μ in about 12 min. at a resolution of approximately 3 cm.$^{-1}$ at 2000 cm.$^{-1}$, using a rock salt prism. They have double-beam photometer units, thus enabling the user to compensate for cell and solvent absorption. For example, if the spectrum of a compound is to be determined in solution, a cell containing the solution would be put in the sample beam and a cell containing an identical path of solvent placed in the reference beam. A moving mirror in the photometer unit causes the two beams to be fed alternately at about 12 c./sec. into the monochromator. Thus, at each wavelength, the detector compares in rapid succession the energy from each beam. The difference between the two amplified signals is fed to a servo system which in turn causes a comb to move in or out of the reference beam until the beams are in balance. The movement of the servo system is displayed on a chart, plotted versus wavelength – i.e., the absorption spectrum.

Sampling

(a) Solids

Two techniques for handling solids are in common use: the mull and the potassium bromide disc. The latter technique involves grinding the solid sample with an excess of alkali halide in a small vibratory mill. The resultant micron-size powder is then strongly compressed *in vacuo* in a die and sintered to a transparent disc. Although widely used, we regard this method as being of only marginal value for most types of work. It is time-consuming and several specific difficulties are known which may ruin the desired spectrum. Inorganic compounds are liable to undergo anion exchange with the alkali halide. In contrast, the mull technique is of wide applicability and is rapid.

The principles of mulling are (i) to reduce the particle size of the solid sample to micron size so that scattering will be low, and (ii) to surround the powder with a matrix of refractive index as near to itself as possible, again reducing scatter. Liquid paraffin ('Nujol') is the usual mulling liquid. It has absorption in certain C—H stretch-and-bend regions (figure 6.1) which obscures similar vibrational absorption in any sample. To observe the obscured parts of the spectrum, a mulling agent which is transparent in these regions is employed. The common ones are hexachlorobutadiene (HCB) and 'Fluorlube', a fluorinated product marketed by I.C.I. Ltd.

To prepare a mull (figure 6.2), place 5–10 mg. of the sample in an

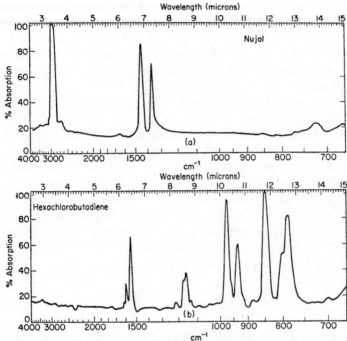

Figure 6.1. The infrared spectrum of (a) liquid paraffin (Nujol) and (b) hexachlorobutadiene.

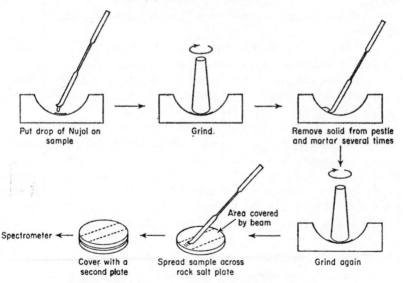

Figure 6.2. Stages in the preparation of a mull.

agate mortar and allow a *small* amount of 'Nujol' to run onto it from the end of a micro spatula. (Do not use a pipette as this is not capable of such fine control.) Make a fairly stiff paste, removing the mull from both pestle and mortar several times, using the spatula. This ensures good grinding and mixing of the layer of solid which sticks to the agate. Gradually thin the paste with 'Nujol' until the consistency is right for the spectrometer to be used. Spread a thin line of sample down the centre of a rock salt plate and cover with a second plate. Mount in a suitable holder in the sample beam. If the mull is too thick and absorbs too strongly, a little may be squeezed out by *gentle pressure*. If this does not work, *start again*. Never grind the plates together in an attempt to thin a mull; you will only damage the plates and they are expensive.

> NOTE Samples containing nitrate and nitrite groups are liable to an ion exchange with the rock salt plates. Check the plates for cleanliness, and re-polish if necessary.

(b) Solutions

It must first be ascertained that a solvent is available which is transparent in the region of interest. If one is available, proceed as follows:

(i) Fill the sample cell (figure 6.3) with solvent. Suck it clean at the pump.

(ii) Refill and empty a further two or three times.

(iii) Fill and place in the spectrometer sample beam.

(iv) Adjust the variable path cell (figure 6.4) (careful! it is expensive) to the same path length as that of the sample cell. Flush with solvent, as above, and fill. Place it in the reference beam.

(v) Run a spectrum over the region of interest. Adjust the variable path cell if necessary, so as to give complete cancellation. (Negative absorption means that the reference cell is thicker than the sample cell.)

(vi) Empty the sample cell and fill it with a dilute solution of the sample. Place it in the instrument.

(vii) Record spectrum.

> NOTE In regions where the solvent is more than 60% absorbent, any solute spectrum must be regarded as unreliable, if indeed any spectrum is obtained in this region.

Figure 6.3. Infrared cell for liquid samples. (By courtesy of
Research and Industrial Instruments Company.)

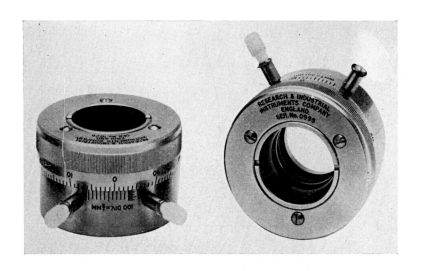

Figure 6.4. Variable path infrared cell. (By courtesy of Research
and Industrial Instruments Company.)

6.1 Preparation and Study of Two Inorganic Isomers

The complex $[Co(NO_2)(NH_3)_5] \cdot Cl_2$ exists in two isomeric forms, Co—NO_2 and Co—ONO. The difference is clearly demonstrated by the infrared spectra of the compounds. Both isomers are prepared from $[CoCl(NH_3)_5]Cl_2$, the product obtained depending on the pH.

(i) *Chloropenta-amminecobalt*(III) *chloride*, $[CoCl(NH_3)_5]Cl_2$

This compound is one of the most important of the cobaltammines and it is the starting substance for the preparation of many coordination complexes of cobalt. Note the ease of oxidation of the hexa-amminecobalt(II) ion.

Dissolve 10 g. cobalt carbonate in the smallest possible amount of concentrated hydrochloric acid, filter, cool and add to a mixture of 125 ml. 10% ammonia and 25 g. ammonium carbonate in 125 ml. water (0·880 ammonia is approximately 30%). Draw a rapid stream of air through the solution by means of a filter pump for about 3 hr., then add 75 g. ammonium chloride and evaporate the oxidized mixture on a water bath until a fairly thick sludge is obtained. Acidify the product with dilute hydrochloric acid, stirring constantly until evolution of carbon dioxide has ceased and the solution is faintly acid. Neutralize with ammonia again and add an excess of 5 ml. 0·880 ammonia. Warm the solution on a water bath for about an hour to ensure the disappearance of any tetra-ammine salts, dilute to 200 ml., add 150 ml. concentrated hydrochloric acid, heat the resultant solution on a water bath for 30–45 min. and cool, when crystals will separate. Filter off the crystals and wash them with dilute hydrochloric acid, then with alcohol. Dry on a porous plate.

(ii) *Nitropenta-amminecobalt*(III) *chloride*, $[Co(NO_2)(NH_3)_5]Cl_2$

Dissolve 5 g. chloropenta-amminecobalt(III) chloride in 50 ml. water to which 12·5 ml. 10% ammonia has been added. Filter, cool and acidify slightly by the addition of dilute hydrochloric acid. Now add 6 g. sodium nitrite and heat until the red precipitate first formed has completely dissolved. Add 65 ml. concentrated hydrochloric acid, cool in ice, collect the brownish-yellow crystals which separate on a filter paper, wash with alcohol and dry in air.

(iii) *Nitritopenta-amminecobalt*(III) *chloride*, $[Co \cdot NO)(NH_3)_5]Cl_2$

Dissolve 2·5 g. chloropenta-amminecobalt(III) chloride by gently warming with 40 ml. water to which 9 ml. 0·880 ammonia has been

7

added. Filter, and neutralize the filtrate with dilute hydrochloric acid. Add 2·5 g. sodium nitrite and then 2·5 ml. hydrochloric acid (1 : 1). A red precipitate will gradually form; filter and wash, first with cold water and then with alcohol.

Isomerization

The two isomers exist in equilibrium, the equilibrium lying much nearer the nitro compound than the nitrito. The latter form changes into the more stable nitro complex after several months. The process may be accelerated either by heating or by mixing a 10% solution of the nitrito compound with an equal volume of concentrated hydrochloric acid.

Distinguish between the isomers by infrared spectroscopy. Calculate the number of vibrations expected for the coordinated —NO_2 group and draw out the rough forms of *all* the modes associated with the $CoNO_2$ moeity including those which you will not observe between 2 and 15 μ. Assign absorption due to the coordinated ammonia molecules.

References

1. R. B. Pentland, J. J. Lane and J. V. Quagliano, *J. Amer. Chem. Soc.*, 1956, **78**, 887.
2. I. R. Beattie and D. P. N. Satchell, *Trans. Faraday Soc.*, 1956, **52**, 1590.
3. D. M. L. Goodgame and M. A. Hitchman, *Inorg. Chem.* 1964, **3**, 1389.

6.2 The Effect of Symmetry on the Infrared Spectrum of the Sulphate Group

Any regular tetrahedral AB_4 molecule or ion should exhibit only two fundamental absorptions in the infrared spectrum. The vibrational modes which give rise to these absorptions may be described roughly as stretching and bending modes; both are triply degenerate. In the case of an ionic sulphate, two strong infrared absorptions are in fact observed. If, in a given crystal, the symmetry of the environment of the sulphate group is less than tetrahedral, then additional weak absorption may be seen due to vibrations which are forbidden when the full tetrahedral symmetry is applicable.

Complexes are known in which the sulphate group is ionic, monodentate or bidentate, and the splitting and changes of intensity of absorption bands due to that group beautifully illustrate the effects of progressively lowering the symmetry of the ion.

Procedure

Record the infrared spectra (5–17 μ) of the following as 'Nujol' mulls:
(i) a simple ionic sulphate,
(ii) $[Co(NH_3)_6]_2(SO_4)_3 \cdot 5 H_2O$,
(iii) $[Co(SO_4)(NH_3)_5]Br_2$,
(iv) $[Co(en)_2(SO_4)]Br$.

NOTE   The spectrometer available to you may not go beyond 15 μ. This does not really matter although you will not see the second band of the sulphate ion (that due to bending of the O—S—O angles) in its various sites. The effect is just as well exhibited by the higher frequency band.

Identify the bands due to the sulphate group in each complex. With the aid of a demonstrator (if necessary) draw out the rough form of the vibrations giving rise to each absorption.

List the symmetry elements of the sulphate groups in each of the three environments.

References

1. K. Nakamoto, *Infrared Spectra of Inorganic and Coordination Compounds*, Wiley, New York, 1963.
2. K. Nakamoto *et. al.*, *J. Amer. Chem. Soc.*, 1957, **79**, 4904.
3. C. G. Barraclough and M. L. Tobe, *J. Chem. Soc.*, **1961**, 1993.

Preparation of complexes

There is no point in preparing the complexes (ii)–(iv) if they are available from a previous experiment or class. Only very small quantities (5 mg.) are needed for spectroscopy so that one preparation of each compound will probably provide enough material for the whole class. The preparations are given below.

(ii) *Hexa-amminecobalt*(III) *sulphate pentahydrate*, $[Co(NH_3)_6]_2$ $(SO_4)_3 \cdot 5 H_2O$.   Dissolve 5 g. $[Co(NH_3)_6]Cl_3$* in 50 ml. hot water and mix with 50 ml. 20% sulphuric acid. Heat the solution to 60°c and add 25 ml. 95% alcohol. Warm for a few minutes on a water bath to dissolve the solid and set aside to crystallize. After 24 hr., crystallization should be complete; wash the crystals at the pump with 95% alcohol until the filtrate is neutral. Dissolve the salt in hot water and precipitate by addition of alcohol. Filter and wash with alcohol until

* Use a stock sample or prepare as in experiment 18.1.

acid-free. Dry in air. If required, further recrystallization may be effected from hot water.

Reference

S. M. Jorgensen, Z. anorg. Chem., 1898, **17**, 455.

(iii) *Sulphatopenta-amminecobalt*(III) *bromide*, $[Co(SO_4)(NH_3)_5]Br$. Stir 10 g. $[CoCl(NH_3)_5]Cl_2$* with 36 g. concentrated sulphuric acid in a porcelain dish: add the acid in small portions so that the evolution of hydrogen chloride gas is not too violent. When evolution has ceased, heat the resulting oily mass on a boiling water bath for 4 hr., during which more hydrogen chloride will be given off. Dilute with water and continue heating on the water bath until there is no more evaporation. Pour the liquid into a beaker and dilute with two volumes of water. If it is necessary to filter, do so as quickly as possible. Stand for 24 hr., whereupon the *acid sulphate* precipitates in good yield as shiny, rectangular violet-red plates. Decant the strongly coloured mother liquor and transfer the crystals to a sintered-glass filter. Wash with 95% alcohol and dry in air.

Dissolve 4 g. *acid sulphate* in 120 ml. cold water and treat the solution with a mixture of 20 ml. concentrated hydrobromic acid (b.p. 126°c) and 80 ml. water. Gradually add alcohol, whilst stirring, to precipitate the product as a fine violet-red crystalline powder. Wash with alcohol until acid-free and dry in air.

Reference

S. M. Jorgensen, J. pract. Chem., 1885, **31**, 270.

(iv) *Bis*(*ethylenediamine*)*sulphatocobalt*(III) *bromide*, $[Co(en)_2 \cdot SO_4]Br$. Add ten grams of *trans*-$[Co(en)_2Cl_2]Cl$ (use a stock sample, or prepare as in experiment 15.1) to 20 ml. concentrated sulphuric acid in a beaker. When the initial effervescence has subsided, heat gently. The complex slowly dissolves with evolution of hydrogen chloride and a violet solution results. Raise the temperature to 120°c until the evolution of gas ceases and then allow the oil to cool. Pour into 1 litre of alcohol which is continually stirred to prevent formation of an oil. Filter off the solid, wash with alcohol and then ether. Dry *in vacuo*.

Dissolve the deliquescent solid in 20 ml. water and treat with 5 g. lithium bromide in 5 ml. water and then leave in a refrigerator at 0°c for three days. Filter off the purple crystals, wash with alcohol

---

* Prepared in experiment 6.1. Use a stock sample if available.

and then ether. Air dry. If the mother liquors are left for a further three days a second crop of $[Co(en)_2H_2O \cdot SO_4]Br \cdot H_2O$ will be obtained.

Heat powdered specimens of the above product at $110°c$ for 24 hr. in an oven. Recrystallize the $[Co(en)_2SO_4]Br$ by dissolution in a *minimum* of cold water and addition of sodium bromide. The product crystallizes as short purple needles.

Reference

C. G. Barraclough and M. L. Tobe, *J. Chem. Soc.*, **1961**, 1993.

6.3 Infrared Spectra of Complexes Containing the NO Group

There are several ways in which the NO group can combine with metal atoms, giving a variety of compounds in which the group may be considered as ranging from NO^+ through neutral NO to NO^-. The infrared stretching frequency of the group is an excellent indicator of the nature of the bonding. Thus, NO^+ may absorb as high as 2220 cm.$^{-1}$ and NO^- as low as 1045 cm.$^{-1}$. Nitric oxide itself absorbs at 1883 cm.$^{-1}$ and examples can be found of NO absorption in complexes at most positions in the range 2000–1600 cm.$^{-1}$.

Procedure

Record the infrared spectra, 2–15 μ, as 'Nujol' mulls, of the following compounds:

  (i) $[NO][SbCl_6]$ or $(NO)_2S_2O_7$,
  (ii) $K_3[Cr(CN)_5NO] \cdot H_2O$,
  (iii) $[Co(NO)(NH_3)_5](NO_3)_2$.

  NOTE After running each spectrum check that the rock salt plates are spectroscopically clean. The NO group will readily penetrate the plates: if this occurs, they must be re-polished (see demonstrator).

Assign (a) a band in each compound due to stretching of the NO group, (b) all other bands observed. Discuss the variation of ν_{NO} in terms of bonding mechanisms.

References

1. C. C. Addison & J. Lewis, *Quart. Rev.*, 1955, **9**, 115.
2. J. Lewis, R. J. Irving and G. Wilkinson, *J. Inorg. Nuclear Chem.*, 1958, **7**, 32.
3. W. P. Griffiths, J. Lewis and G. Wilkinson, *Ibid.*, p. 38.

Preparations

Do not spend time preparing more than *one* of the compounds needed. If they are all available from laboratory stock, so much the better. The preparations of [NO][SbCl$_6$] and (NO)$_2 \cdot$S$_2$O$_7$ are described in experiments 8.1 and 8.2 respectively. The chromium and cobalt complexes may be prepared as follows.

(i) *Potassium pentacyanonitrosylchromate monohydrate, $K_3[Cr(CN)_5$ $NO]H_2O$.* Dissolve 2·5 g. chromium trioxide in 15 ml. water containing 7 g. potassium hydroxide. Cool in ice and add a saturated solution containing 12 g. potassium cyanide. Filter the solution and add to the filtrate 3 g. hydroxylamine hydrochloride. Heat on a steam bath for 2 hr., filter and cool. Pour the filtrate into 100 ml. ethanol with stirring. Filter and dissolve the precipitate in the minimum quantity of water; re-precipitate with ethanol. Recrystallize from water.

Reference

W. P. Griffith, J. Lewis and G. Wilkinson, *J. Chem. Soc.*, **1959**, 872.

(ii) *Nitrosylpenta-amminecobalt*(III) *nitrate, $[Co(NO)(NH_3)_5](NO_3)_2$.* Treat a solution of 8 g. hydrated cobalt nitrate in 20 ml. water with 50 ml. 0·880 ammonia. Filter. Pass nitric oxide through the solution for 3 hr. in the absence of air. Recrystallize the red salt twice from dilute ammonia.

Reference

W. P. Griffith, J. Lewis & G. Wilkinson, *J. Inorg. Nuclear Chem.*, 1958, **7**, 38.

Chapter 7

High-Temperature Preparations

One of the most common uses of high temperatures in synthetic work is in the preparation of metal halides. The general procedure involves passing the halogen (possibly in a carrier gas) over the heated metal or an oxide–carbon mixture. Many variants of procedure and technique have been recorded; the particular form of the apparatus used will depend largely upon the volatility of the reagents and products involved.

7.1 Preparation of Titanium Tetrabromide, TiBr₄

$$TiO_2 + 2\,C + 2\,Br_2 \rightarrow TiBr_4 + 2\,CO$$

Assemble the apparatus shown in figure 7.1. Bottle C contains concentrated sulphuric acid. Forty-five grams of bromine are introduced into D. The combustion tube is of Pyrex and contains at its centre a Pyrex boat holding an intimate mixture of 10 g. titanium(IV) oxide and 6 g. sugar charcoal.

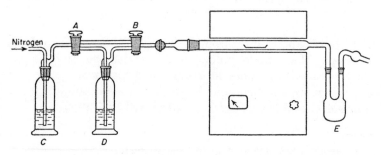

Figure 7.1. Apparatus for the preparation of titanium tetrabromide.

73

Pass a moderate stream of dry nitrogen through the by-pass AB and bring the furnace up to 300°c for about 30 min. This will dry the apparatus and reactants and moisture will collect in E. Remove this by flaming and then attach a drying tube to E. Close by-pass AB, thereby passing nitrogen through the bromine and into the furnace, which is now brought to 550°c, and reduce the flow of nitrogen by about half. Cool E in ice to condense the solid titanium tetrabromide. When reaction is complete (approximately 4 hr.), switch off the furnace and open by-pass AB. Warm E to about 100°c. The flow of nitrogen removes excess bromine vapour. Maintaining the flow of nitrogen, remove E from the reaction tube and quickly close it with a glass stopper. Replace the drying tube by the apparatus in figure 7.2.

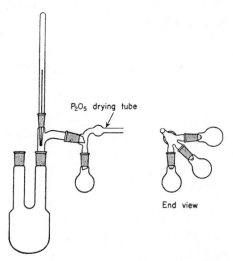

P₂O₅ drying tube

End view

Figure 7.2. Apparatus for the distillation of titanium tetrabromide.

Distil the titanium tetrabromide (b.p. 230°c; m.p. 39°c). Remove and stopper the sample bulb(s) and transfer the amber-coloured product to tared ampoules in a dry-bag (this must be very dry). The product is a crystalline hygroscopic solid, soluble in many organic solvents but very readily hydrolyzed by water.

Exercises

1. Determine the bromide content of your product.
2. Suggest a method for the preparation of titanium tetraiodide. Discuss this with the demonstrator before preparing about 5 g. product.

3. How would you expect titanium tetrahalides to react with Lewis bases?
What methods would you apply to elucidate the structures of the compounds
so formed. (See *Quart. Rev.*, 1963, **17**, 382.)
4. Titanium tribromide is easily prepared from titanium tetrabromide by
reduction with hydrogen. What is its crystal structure?

7.2 Preparation of Vanadium Tetrachloride and Vanadium Trichloride, VCl₄ and VCl₃

$$V + 2 Cl_2 \rightarrow VCl_4$$

$$2 VCl_4 + S_2Cl_2 \rightarrow 2 VCl_3 + 2 SCl_2$$

Assemble the apparatus as shown in figure 7.3. The end, *A*, of the

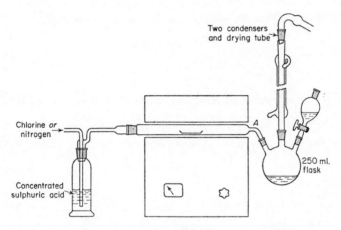

Figure 7.3. Apparatus for the preparation of vanadium tetrachloride and vanadium trichloride.

reaction tube should be kept as close to the furnace as possible as
product tends to condense before reaching the flask. Ten grams of
vanadium metal powder is placed in a porcelain boat in the centre
of the reaction tube. Flush the apparatus with dry nitrogen for
about half an hour, raising the temperature to 300°c. Stop the nitrogen flow and fix a drying tube to the condenser. Chlorine is now
passed (from a cylinder) and the temperature brought up to 450°c.
The chlorine may be diluted with nitrogen if the product tends to
form too quickly. It may also be necessary to flame the delivery tube
leading to the flask, which should be cooled in ice. At the end of the
reaction (approximately 4 hr.) switch off the furnace and maintain a

slow stream of nitrogen through the apparatus. When cool, quickly remove the delivery tube and replace it with a glass stopper. Slowly run in an excess of disulphur dichloride (see Appendix 2 for the technique of opening a large ampoule). Warm the mixture and allow to reflux for 12 hr. Then remove volatile products by (a) distillation and (b) evacuation on a vacuum line (not a water pump) with gentle heating to 80°c by means of an oil bath. Using a good dry-bag, transfer the resulting deep-purple solid to tared ampoules. Yield, approximately 29 g.

NOTE   It is most important to exclude moisture during this preparation as non-volatile contaminants will otherwise be formed.

Exercises

1. Determine the chloride content of a portion of the product.
2. What is the structure of VCl₃?
3. What happens when VCl₃ is heated strongly?

7.3 Preparation of Molybdenum Pentachloride, MoCl₅

Assemble in a fume cupboard the apparatus shown in figure 7.4 and charge the tube with 6 g. molybdenum powder. Pass hydrogen

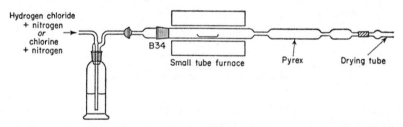

Figure 7.4. Apparatus for the preparation of molybdenum penta-chloride.

chloride gas (from a cylinder, or prepared as in experiment 11.3) mixed with nitrogen through the apparatus until all the air is swept out and then gently heat the metal in a slow stream of the gas. Water and a cloudy sublimate of MoO₃·2 HCl will be formed and should be removed from the apparatus by gentle flaming. Continue until no more sublimate forms. Cool in a stream of hydrogen chloride.

Fit a calcium chloride guard tube to the open end of the reaction tube. Attach a chlorine cylinder in place of the hydrogen chloride supply, taking care to flush out the delivery tube, and pass a slow stream of chlorine–nitrogen over the molybdenum. If the reaction does not begin of its own accord warm gently until the deep-red vapour of MoCl$_5$ appears and fine crystals deposit beyond the first constriction. *Gently* flame the tube to keep the constrictions clear and distribute the product between the two receiving sections. When all the metal has burnt off turn off the furnace and cool whilst passing a slow stream of nitrogen. Seal off at the constrictions using a fairly fine jet (*not* a Bunsen burner). Replace the calcium chloride tube with a rubber bung.

Exercises

1. What is the structure of MoCl$_5$ in (i) the gas phase, (ii) the solid state?

2. Why is hydrogen chloride passed over the heated metal during the first part of the experiment?

3. Investigate the following aspects of the chemistry of MoCl$_5$, using a good dry-box (or bag) as it is very sensitive to moisture. Use the small receiver section sealed with the rubber bung.

(i) Add a few crystals, one at a time, to a small quantity of boiled-out water. Explain the result.

(ii) Dissolve MoCl$_5$ in a small quantity of ether. Isolate any product and record its infrared spectrum. Say what you can about its structure.

(iii) Using freshly distilled dry carbon disulphide as solvent add a solution of phenol to one of MoCl$_5$. Remove the solvent by evacuation and recrystallize from a small amount of benzene. Explain the result.

Chapter 8

Vacuum-Line Preparations

Many operations and preparations are conveniently carried out under vacuum. It is often the easiest way to exclude oxygen or other potential reactants. Before attempting any experiments involving the use of the vacuum line you must be thoroughly familiar with the technique of operation described below.

General high-vacuum technique

A good *rotary pump* will produce a vacuum of approximately 5×10^{-3} mm. mercury in a leak-free glass system. This is adequate for most preparative work. Vacua of 10^{-6} mm. mercury are readily attained with a mercury or oil *diffusion pump* backed by a rotary pump and may be necessary in some cases, particularly when reactants or products are likely to be decomposed by the traces of water remaining in the glass line at rotary pump pressure.

SAFETY NOTES (i) The exhaust of all rotary pumps should be led *via* a tube to a fume cupboard or window. This is always good practice but it is vital with a vacuum pump used for preparative work. Failure to observe this simple precaution has led to fatal accidents. (ii) It is wise to wear safety glasses when operating a vacuum line.

Demountable joints may be either conical or hemispherical in shape, figure 8.1, the latter being used when some bending must be allowed. They are lubricated with a thin film of a grease having a low vapour pressure. The choice of grease depends upon the temperature to which any part of the line is to be heated and on the chemical nature of the compounds which will be in contact with it. The properties of some commonly used greases are given in Table 8.1.

Table 8.1

Grease	Chemical type	Remarks
Apiezon N	Hydrocarbon	Maximum working temperature 35°c
„ L	„	Vapour pressure 10⁻³ mm. mercury at 300°c
„ T	„	Maximum working temperature 120°c
Silicone	Silicone	Suitable for high-vacuum use
Kel-F	Fluorochlorocarbon	Valuable for experiments with fluorinated compounds

It is sometimes desirable to make demountable joints semi-permanent and for this purpose a hydrocarbon wax is generally used, e.g., Picien or Apiezon W40, which soften at about 80° and 40°c respectively.

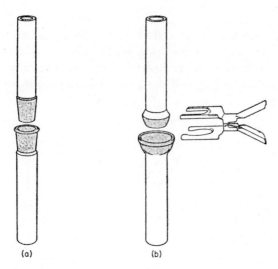

(a)   (b)

Figure 8.1. Ground-glass joints: (a) cone and socket; (b) ball and socket with clip.

The most reliable way of joining glass parts is to make a fused seal. A few basic operations on glass-ware are described in Appendix 2. You will not need to know anything more about the technique of glass work for purposes of this course.

Two common types of *high-vacuum tap* are illustrated in figure 8.2.
Type 2 is often preferred; there is less likelihood of a leak occurring
since air pressure forces the key into the barrel when the line is
evacuated.

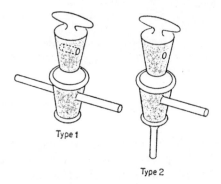

Figure 8.2. High-vacuum taps: (1) straight bore; (2) 'L' shape.

To grease a tap, run a layer of grease down each side of the key,
insert this into the barrel and rotate gently to distribute the grease.
NEVER turn an ungreased tap. When, for chemical reasons, grease
cannot be tolerated, there are two alternatives: either a greaseless
valve or a mercury cut-off may be used. Typical designs are shown
in figure 8.3.

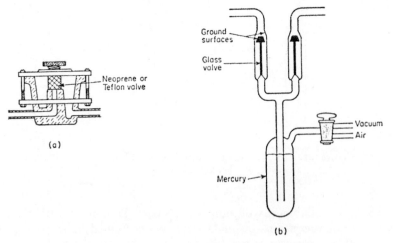

Figure 8.3. Greaseless taps for vacuum lines: (a) greaseless valve;
(b) a mercury cut-off.

In every vacuum line a *cold trap* is placed immediately before the pump (diffusion or rotary), the usual coolant being liquid nitrogen (b.p. $-195°c$). This prevents (a) condensable vapours from reaching the pump and being dissolved in the oil with consequent raising of its vapour pressure and a decrease in pump efficiency,* and (b) prevents back-streaming of vapours from the pumps to the vacuum line.

Pressure measurement in the range 10^{-1} to 10^{-6} mm. mercury is generally by means of a McLeod gauge in which a large volume of gas (say 200 ml.) is compressed to a small but measurable volume in a capillary tube. For use with preparative vacuum lines a 'Vacustat' gauge is sufficiently accurate. Pressures greater than 1 mm. are conviently measured on a simple manometer.

Leak testing should be carried out when a new line or section is used for the first time. Evacuate the line to rotary pump vacuum and inspect all fused-glass joints with a 'Tesla' high-frequency probe. A violet discharge (colour depending upon the pressure in the line) will be observed. The discharge from the probe will be drawn towards any 'pin-hole' leaks when the probe is run over the affected area.

The vacuum line that you will use is illustrated in figure 8.4.

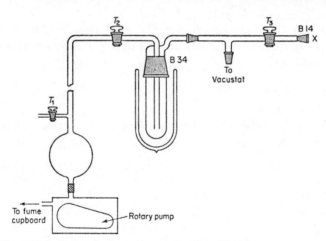

Figure 8.4. General-purpose vacuum line. Further units can be added at X; see figures 8.5, 8.6 and 8.8.

Further units will be added at X, depending upon the experiment to be performed.

---

* Pumps fitted with 'gas ballast' are designed to pump a limited amount of condensable vapours, but, inevitably, some vapour is condensed into the oil. A poorer vacuum is the sacrifice made for the facility to pump vapours.

The line is built of small, demountable units because experience has shown that the inevitable breakages which occur during a course cause least disruption and loss of time if a spare section can be fitted by the student. In a line containing only fused-glass joints the alternative is to clean the line thoroughly, cut out the damaged section, wait for a glass blower, etc.!

Operation is as follows

1. *Starting up*

We assume that the whole line is at atmospheric pressure and all taps are closed except the air-inlet tap T_1.

(i) Ensure that all taps, and the conical joint on the trap, are properly greased and free-moving. Consult a demonstrator if they are not.

(ii) Close T_1 and switch on the pump. Check that the pump is working properly and that it has sufficient oil in the reservoir.

(iii) Open tap T_2 *gently*.

(iv) When the bulk of the air has been removed, place a Dewar flask of liquid nitrogen around the cold trap. Remember to top-up the Dewar from time to time.

(v) Measure the pressure by rotating the 'Vacustat' to its working position. It should be $\leqslant 0.1$ mm. mercury before you continue with the experiment.

2. *Closing down*

(i) Close all taps.

(ii) Switch off the rotary pump and open tap T_1 *immediately*.

(iii) Remove the Dewar of liquid nitrogen from the trap.

PRECAUTIONS Although Pyrex-glass apparatus is fairly robust, it can, of course, be broken by careless or clumsy handling. The following precautions *must be taken*.

(i) When turning vacuum taps use *both hands*, one to steady the barrel and the other to turn the key. If the laboratory is cold the grease on the taps may be very stiff. Before attempting to turn the taps they must be warmed *gently* with a hot air blower (or hair dryer).

(ii) Always consider carefully the consequences of opening a tap. Do nothing suddenly on a vacuum line. This is particularly important with apparatus containing mercury. To set a column of mercury in rapid motion in a glass apparatus is equivalent to hitting it with a hammer!

(iii) A trap cooled in liquid nitrogen is at a temperature below that of liquid oxygen. If air is let into this trap liquid oxygen will condense in it leading to two possible hazards: (a) an explosion hazard if a readily oxidizable condensate is already in the trap (c.f., rocket fuels!); (b) if the trap is closed off and allowed to warm up the liquid oxygen will vapourize and the resulting pressure will shatter both apparatus and bystander. Consequently, liquid nitrogen Dewars must always be removed before air is let into the trap. If large quantities of air have to be pumped out through the trap it should not be cooled until after the air has been removed.

8.1 Preparation of Nitrosonium Hexachlorantimonate, [NO][SbCl₆]

Many salts containing the nitrosonium cation can be prepared by reacting nitrosyl chloride with an anhydrous halide. For example,

$$NOCl + SbCl_5 \rightarrow [NO][SbCl_6]$$

These compounds are moisture-sensitive and must be handled only in a dry-box. Read the general instructions on vacuum technique (pp. 78) before proceeding.

Procedure

(i) Prepare 3–4 g. nitrosyl chloride by the action of excess nitrosyl sulphuric acid* on 6–7 g. sodium chloride. Collect the gaseous nitrosyl chloride in a trap fitted with a calcium chloride guard tube, cooled in an acetone–solid carbon dioxide bath. Connect the trap to the vacuum line in the position shown in figure 8.5. Close T_4 and freeze the liquid gas in C by surrounding the trap with a Dewar of liquid nitrogen. Evacuate C.

(ii) Using a dry-bag, transfer approximately 2 ml. antimony penta-chloride to bulb A, which must then be stoppered.

NOTE If it is necessary to open a new ampoule of antimony pentachloride use the method of Appendix 2.

Connect the bulb to the vacuum line, freeze in liquid nitrogen, and evacuate. Close T_4 and allow A to warm to room temperature.

* Made by passing sulphur dioxide slowly through fuming nitric acid; cool in ice–salt to keep the temperature down to 5°c.

Freeze it in liquid nitrogen again and re-open T_4. This ensures that trapped air is released from the liquid.

(iii) With T_4 closed, distil the antimony pentachloride into B, which should be cooled in liquid nitrogen. Then open T_4 and distil the nitrosyl chloride into B. Allow B to warm up in a slush bath of

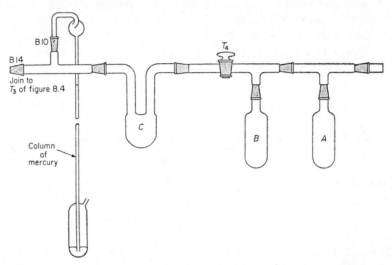

Figure 8.5. Apparatus for the preparation of nitrosonium hexachlorantimonate.

carbon tetrachloride–liquid nitrogen ($-23°c$). Note the solubility of the product in liquid nitrosyl chloride. Re-freeze C and thereby distil excess solvent from B to C. Admit dry air or nitrogen to the apparatus and remove B to a dry-bag. Transfer the solid product to tared ampoules.

Exercises

1. Determine the chloride content of a sample after hydrolysis. Explain why your result is several per cent below the theoretical figure.
2. Record the infrared spectrum of a sample in the range 2300–1700 cm.$^{-1}$, making the mull in a dry-bag. Compare the NO^+ stretching frequency with that of other nitrosonium salts.

NOTE   Commercial 'Nujol' or liquid paraffin may contain enough moisture to hydrolyze the sample. Better results can be obtained using hexachlorobutadiene as the mulling agent. Protect the rock salt plates of the 'Nujol' cell from the mull (which will exchange NO^+ for Na^+ with the plate) by thin discs of polythene.

Reference

D. W. A. Sharp and J. Thorley, *J. Chem. Soc.*, **1963**, 3557.

8.2 Preparation of Nitrosonium Pyrosulphate, $(NO)_2S_2O_7$

Dinitrogen tetroxide reacts with sulphur dioxide under pressure at room temperature to form nitrosonium pyrosulphate.

$$2 N_2O_4 + 2 SO_2 \rightarrow (NO)_2S_2O_7 + N_2O_3$$

Read the general instructions on vacuum technique (pp. 78), and Appendix 2, before starting the experiment.

Procedure

(i) Prepare about 3 ml. dinitrogen tetroxide by heating lead nitrate and collect the gas in a trap, A, cooled in acetone solid carbon dioxide. The trap should contain phosphorus pentoxide and be protected from the atmosphere by a calcium chloride guard tube. Connect A to the vacuum line as shown in figure 8.6 and join the

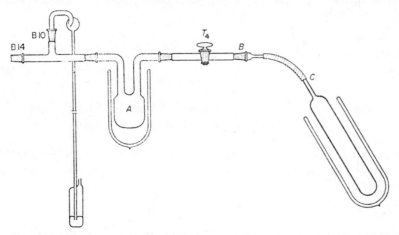

Figure 8.6. Apparatus for the preparation of nitrosonium pyrosulphate.

Carius tube to B by about one foot of pressure tubing. With A cooled in liquid nitrogen evacuate the apparatus. Then close T_3, remove the coolant form A, and distil the dinitrogen tetroxide into the Carius tube which is now frozen. Close T_4 and remove trap A from the line.

(ii) Condense about 3 ml. sulphur dioxide from a syphon into another trap, A', containing phosphorus pentoxide and fitted with a calcium chloride guard tube. Connect A' to the vacuum line, freeze, evacuate and distil into the still frozen Carius tube.

(iii) Check that the Carius tube is fully evacuated and then, *under the supervision of a demonstrator*, seal it off at C. Anneal the end thoroughly. The tube should be well wrapped in a cloth and left in a fume cupboard for 24 hr. or more.

(iv) Using a glass-knife, score around the top of the tube. Freeze in liquid nitrogen, and crack-off with a piece of hot glass rod (see Appendix 2). Immediately reconnect to the already evacuated line by the pressure tubing, open T_4, remove the coolant from the tube and pump off the gaseous material. Finally, remove the tube to a dry-bag and transfer the white solid salt to tared ampoules. Retain samples for analysis and infrared spectroscopy.

Exercises

1. Determine the sulphate content after hydrolysis.
2. Record the infrared spectrum (see notes above relating to experiment 8.1) and compare the position of the NO^+ stretching frequency with that of other nitrosonium salts.

Reference

D. W. A. Sharp and J. Thorley, *J. Chem. Soc.*, **1963**, 3557.

8.3 Preparation of Perchloryl Fluoride, ClO_3F, and Determination of its Molecular Weight

This compound is a condensable gas which can be conveniently handled and purified on a vacuum line. Its molecular weight will be determined.

Preparation

The apparatus shown in figure 8.7 should be assembled. Seven grams of potassium perchlorate in the 250 ml. round-bottom flask are treated with 70 g. fluorosulphonic acid (technical grade) from the dropping funnel.

> SAFETY NOTE   When handling fluorosulphonic acid wear rubber gloves as it can burn the skin severely. At the end of the experiment, wash your hands whilst wearing the gloves.

Stir slowly during the addition and gently raise the temperature. At about 50°c perchloryl fluoride will begin to come off. Continue warming gently to about 85°c. Pass the gas *over* the solution in

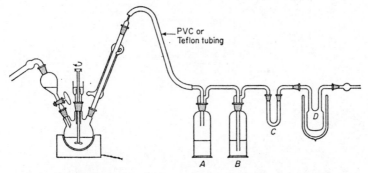

Figure 8.7. Apparatus for the preparation of perchloryl fluoride.

trap A (10% aqueous sodium hydroxide containing 5% sodium thiosulphate) and *through* a similar solution in B. The potassium hydroxide pellets in C dry the product which is then condensed in trap D cooled in acetone–solid carbon dioxide.

Reference

G. Barth-Wehrenalp, *J. Inorg. Nuclear Chem.*, 1956, **2** 266.

Purification and molecular weight determination

Remove trap D and protect both openings with drying tubes. Connect to a vacuum line assembled as in figure 8.8. Purify the perchloryl fluoride as follows. Cool D in liquid nitrogen and, with T_4, T_5 and T_6 open, evacuate the apparatus. Close T_6 and T_3. Allow D to warm up slowly and cool E, thereby distilling the liquefied gas. Open T_3 and pump again. Close T_3, T_4 and open T_5, T_6. Allow E to warm up slowly until the manometer registers a pressure of about 450 mm. mercury. Close T_6 and re-cool E in liquid nitrogen. Remove flask F^* from the line (wipe grease off the joint) and weigh. Calculate the molecular weight of your sample. (N.B. You will also need to know the weight of F when evacuated, and its volume. The latter can be determined by weighing F when filled with acetone.) Discuss sources of error in this determination.

* This should be of approximately 100–130 ml. volume.

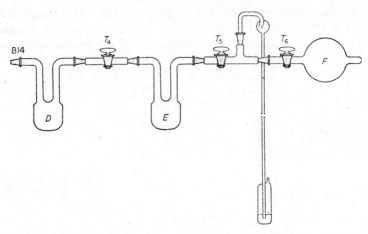

Figure 8.8. Apparatus for purification and molecular weight
determination of perchloryl fluoride.

Exercises

Look up the infrared spectrum of ClO_3F (*J. Chem. Phys.*, 1956, **25**, 1128).
Draw out the normal modes of vibration of the molecule.

Chapter 9

Inert-Atmosphere Technique

There are many instances in which it is not permissible to carry out a chemical or physical process in contact with the atmosphere, usually because a reactant is sensitive to oxidation or hydrolysis. In such cases an inert atmosphere must be provided, or it might be preferable to work *in vacuo*. The choice in any particular instance will depend upon the nature of the reaction and reactants, their sensitivity to moisture, oxygen, etc., and the available equipment. The use of inert atmospheres in chemistry and metallurgy, already important, is constantly increasing. A major stimulant has been the atomic energy industry and the need to handle and fabricate parts in new materials. Large inert-atmosphere machining rooms have been built by some firms, operatives entering through locks, wearing breathing gear.

It is important to specify, if possible, the maximum permissible levels of the atmospheric constituents. This may only be an approximate indication. Thus, nitrosonium hexachlorantimonate, p. 83, may be handled readily in a dry-box using phosphorus pentoxide as desiccant, whereas some volatile fluorides, for example, are only safe if handled in a baked-out vacuum line. A vacuum of $1·5 \times 10^{-2}$ mm. mercury is equivalent to an inert atmosphere containing 20 p.p.m. of active impurity.

If it is decided that an inert atmosphere offers the best solution to a given problem, there is still the choice of using either a 'dry-box' or glass apparatus in which an inert atmosphere is maintained. Although some operations (e.g., distillation) are routinely carried out in standard apparatus filled with nitrogen, this method often becomes cumbersome, especially when filtrations and other transfer operations must be performed. It may be worth constructing special apparatus if the process is to be carried out on many occasions; see, for example, experiment 11.8. The preparation of chromous acetate,

89

described below, should be compared with that of *Inorg. Synth.*, **3**, 148, in which all-glass equipment is used.

For many problems, a '*dry-box*' is highly convenient, as normal operations and techniques may be used without modification. If moisture is the only danger, the box may be air-filled and dried with a suitable desiccant. If oxygen and/or moisture is the hazard, nitrogen or argon are commonly used to flush the box. Many types of dry-box have been described in the literature, and several are available commercially. For synthetic studies, a type of box developed by I.C.I. Ltd. has many advantages (figure 9.1). The entry chamber is large enough to permit the introduction of apparatus, but small enough to be flushed free of atmosphere in four minutes. Many dry-boxes, including some commercial types, have large vacuum entry chambers. Although these have their uses, they are often inconvenient and unnecessary. A more logical alternative is the vacuum dry-box: this can be completely evacuated (the gloves being protected by cover plates) and then re-filled with a suitable atmosphere. They are expensive.

Since even small dry-boxes generally cost at least £100, much of your work requiring an inert atmosphere will be done in a *polythene dry-bag** (figure 9.2), which will be suitable for most operations. Whichever piece of equipment you use, dust your hands well with talcum powder (unscented!) before putting them in the gloves.

Dry-bag procedure

Remove one glove and introduce all apparatus and materials necessary for the job in hand. Replace the glove and gently collapse the bag. Inflate with nitrogen from a cylinder, taking care not to fill to too high a pressure – the bag should always feel flabby. Turn off the nitrogen. Collapse the bag by squeezing *gently*. Repeat this procedure three times. The bag is then ready for use.

Dry-box procedure

The large dry-boxes (figure 9.1) are prepared for use as follows: introduce a polythene bag sufficiently large that it fills the box when inflated. Open the outlet valve and inflate the collapsed polythene bag with nitrogen, thereby expelling air from the box. Turn off the nitrogen, remove the bag from its nipple and collapse it, expelling its content into the box. Re-connect to the nitrogen inlet and repeat the process twice. This is much more economical on nitrogen than flushing the box.

* Bags similar to that in figure 9.2 are available from D. R. Grey Ltd., Instrument Division, Carrow Hill, Norwich.

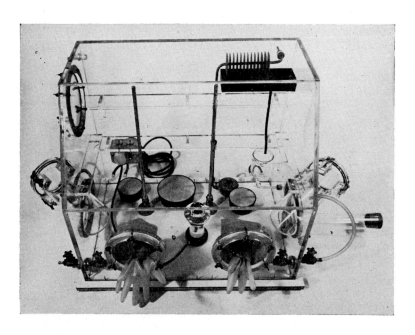

Figure 9.1. A Perspex dry-box for preparative work. (By courtesy
of I.C.I. Ltd., Heavy Organic Chemicals Division.)

Figure 9.2. A polythene dry-bag in use.

Filtration

Filtration in a dry bag may be effected by using a pipette filler attached to the suction nipple of a Buchner filter flask.

Alternatively, a vacuum lead may be sealed into the bag or box. When using such a facility, pass nitrogen into the bag to compensate for that removed by the pump.

Infrared sampling

It is often necessary to prepare a mull or solution for spectroscopy, in the dry-box. *Solutions* present no special difficulty. *Mulls* should be made in the usual way (see p. 64). If the compound under investigation is not too air-sensitive, it will probably be quite safe to mount the mull between two rock salt plates as usual. A small amount of decomposition may occur around the edges. In other cases, a thin strip of 'Scotch Tape' may be run around the edge of the plates, sealing the mull from the air. Transfer the plates to and from the spectrometer in a small nitrogen filled bottle.

Weighing

Weighing in a dry-bag or box is generally unnecessary, given adequate forethought. A balance takes up too much of the already limited space, and will, in any case, be exposed to a rather corrosive atmosphere. Let us suppose that a product in a dry-box is to be ampouled. The following steps are necessary:

(i) Remove the top of the ampoule by making a neat scratch around it with a glass-knife. Snap it off by hand. (See Appendix 2).

(ii) Stick a small label onto the ampoule and then weigh. Pencil the weight on the label.

(iii) Take the ampoules into the dry-box and fill them. Plug the necks with cotton wool.

(iv) Remove from the dry-box and quickly seal off with a glass working torch fitted with a fine jet. Do *not* use a Bunsen burner.

(v) Weigh the sealed ampoule *together with* the removed top portion (minus cotton wool).

(vi) Calculate the weight of compound contained and record on the label.

It is important to know the weight of compound in an ampoule, especially if the compound is likely to be used in a reaction. Thus, the whole of the contents of the ampoule may be used and other reactants calculated accordingly. You will be able to work out other such points of technique as and when necessary.

9.1 Preparation of Chromous Acetate, $Cr(CH_3 \cdot CO_2)_2 \cdot H_2O$

Chromium(II) salts are extremely sensitive to oxidation and must be prepared under an inert atmosphere. Before starting the preparation, check that your 'dry-box' (or bag) is in good condition and well flushed with nitrogen. Water for use in the box should be boiled and cooled under nitrogen. Solvents should be distilled under nitrogen.

Procedure

Place 17·0 g. zinc in a beaker* and add a solution of 10 g. hydrated chromic chloride, $CrCl_3 \cdot 6 H_2O$, in 11·6 ml. water. Pour in 23·0 ml. concentrated hydrochloric acid and cover the beaker with a watch glass. After about 15 min. the solution will have turned blue. Rinse the watch glass, filter the solution in a Buchner funnel and rinse with water. Immediately add a slurry of 27·5 g. sodium acetate in 35·5 ml. water. Stir with a glass rod until the red chromium(II) acetate is precipitated. Filter, and wash several times with small portions of water until the washings are free of chloride. Wash finally with a little ethanol, followed by a little ether. Record the yield and ampoule a portion of the product.

Chromous acetate is a good starting material for the preparation of other chromium(II) salts. Use a portion of your product to prepare the double salt *chromous hydrazine sulphate*, $CrSO_4 \cdot (N_2H_4)_2 \cdot H_2SO_4 \cdot H_2O$, as follows.

To a suspension of chromous acetate in water, add a solution of hydrazine sulphate† in boiling water (30 ml. for each gram hydrazine sulphate). Then add 3N sulphuric acid *very slowly* until, on shaking, the red solid just dissolves to a dull-blue solution. From this, a clean-blue crystalline precipitate of the double salt will settle out over about 2 hr. Once formed, it is air-stable. Wash, as above, with water and then ethanol. Dry in air.

Exercises

1. Determine chromium in the double salt.
2. Investigate the chemistry of chromium(II) beginning with chromous acetate. Prepare and submit a sample of chromous sulphate.
3. From the infrared spectrum of the double salt, say what you can about its structure.
4. What is the solid state structure of chromous acetate? Why is it red, although chromium(II) solutions are blue, and why is it diamagnetic?

* The procedure is that of *Inorg. Synth.*, **6**, 144.
† Calculate quantities according to the amount of chromous acetate taken.

9.2 Preparation of Anhydrous Halides and Complex Halides

Anhydrous halides may be prepared by a variety of methods. It is often convenient, however, to be able to prepare them from a readily available hydrated halide, expecially as many anhydrous halides are hygroscopic. Treatment of a hydrated halide with thionyl chloride is a method of wide applicability and is particularly convenient as the non-metallic products are volatile.

$$MCl_n \cdot x\ H_2O + x\ SOCl_2 \rightarrow MCl_n + x\ SO_2 + 2x\ HCl$$

Near its boiling point, thionyl chloride begins to decompose according to the scheme

$$12\ SOCl_2 \rightarrow 3\ S_2Cl_2 + 6\ SO_2 + 9\ Cl_2$$

For this reason the solvent acts as an oxidizing medium and is therefore unsuitable for dehydration of halides which are susceptible to oxidation.

(i) Using the following procedure, prepare one or more *anhydrous halides* from their hydrated forms. (Discuss your choice with the demonstrator before beginning. It is often convenient to prepare a halide which can be used in another experiment, e.g., $CoCl_2$ for the cobalticinium preparation, experiment 11.4, or $CrCl_3$ for experiment 10·2.)

Place 10 g. finely powdered hydrated halide in a round-bottom flask and add 30 ml. *freshly distilled* thionyl chloride. Fit a condenser to the flask and, when evolution of sulphur dioxide and hydrogen chloride has ceased, reflux under nitrogen for about 2 hr. Distil off excess thionyl chloride *in vacuo* with a nitrogen bleed. Remove final traces of solvent on a vacuum line with gentle heating. Transfer to a dry-box and ampoule.

(ii) Many *complex halides* are hygroscopic and are therefore best prepared in a dry-box. Prepare one or more of the following.

(a) *Preparation of* $[NEt_4]_2[MCl_4]$, $M = Co,\ Ni,\ Cu$*

Reflux the calculated quantity of metal halide with a slight excess of tetraethylammonium chloride (1 g.) in 20 ml. freshly distilled thionyl chloride until dissolution is complete. Stopper the flask and transfer to a N_2 dry-box. Filter and remove solvent by evacuation, using a splash head. Add 10 ml. acetic anhydride to the residue. Filter and wash the solid with small portions of acetic anhydride. Place in an ampoule and dry finally on the vacuum line at 0·1 mm. mercury.

* Tetramethylammonium salts may be used as a cheaper alternative.

(b) *Preparation of* $[NEt_4]_3[Cr_2Cl_9]$

This complex is extremely sensitive to air and should only be prepared if your dry-box and technique are good. Decomposition will be indicated by colour changes.

Proceed as in (a) but do not remove all the thionyl chloride: concentrate to about 10 ml. Refrigeration of the solution will produce crystals of the deep-violet product, which should be filtered and washed with small portions of thionyl chloride. Place in an ampoule and dry as above.

Exercises

1. Review the methods available for the preparation of anhydrous metal halides.
2. Determine the magnetic moment of one of the complexes in (a).
3. How does the structure of the $[CuCl_4]^{2-}$ ion differ from that of its cobalt and nickel analogues? Why?
4. What is the structure of the $[Cr_2Cl_9]^{3-}$ ion; list analogous ions.

Reference

D. M. Adams *et. al.*, *J. Chem. Soc.*, **1963**, 2189.

9.3 Preparation of Sodium Hyponitrite, $Na_2N_2O_2 \cdot 5\,H_2O$

This experiment may be carried out either as described below or in a dry-bag.

Procedure

Wash 4 g. sodium in ether to free it from paraffin and cut it into very small lumps. Add piece by piece to 22 ml. mercury in a clean, dry, 250 ml. beaker in a fume cupboard. Cover the beaker with a gauze as much as possible, and between each addition of sodium, stir the mercury well. *Safety glasses must be worn* during this experiment.

Dissolve 4 g. sodium nitrite in 12 ml. water contained in a 250 ml. two-neck round-bottom flask and immerse in ice water. Pass a steady stream of nitrogen through the flask and slowly add the sodium amalgam with constant agitation of the flask. Transfer the mixture – in a stream of nitrogen to prevent absorption of carbon dioxide – to a separating funnel and shake thoroughly, frequently allowing the hydrogen to escape. When no further gas is liberated and the reduction is complete, leave the separating funnel for about half an hour to allow mercury droplets to settle.

Run off the mercury and then run the liquor into another beaker containing 50 ml. of ethyl alcohol, keeping the tip of the separating funnel beneath the surface of the alcohol to avoid exposure to the atmosphere. Any liquor and crystals adhering to the walls of the funnel can be quickly washed through with 5 ml. water. Stir vigorously for several minutes until the lower syrupy layer is transformed into a paste, which on trituration with a glass rod produces a mass of white crystals. Filter on a sintered glass filter, wash with several small portions of ethyl alcohol and then with ether. Remove occluded ether in a vacuum desiccator. The product may be recrystallized by dissolution in water followed by reprecipitation with ethyl alcohol. Dry as above. Clean the mercury by carefully washing with water and then dilute nitric acid.

Exercises

1. Examine the effect of the following reagents on solutions of sodium hyponitrite and explain your observations:
   (a) an acidimetric indicator,
   (b) silver nitrate,
   (c) dilute hydrochloric acid,
   (d) acidified potassium permanganate,
   (e) alkaline potassium permanganate.
2. Either:
   (a) determine the sodium content by means of a flame photometer,
or
   (b) determine the hyponitrite content gravimetrically as $Ag_2N_2O_2$. Weigh out a sample of dried sodium hyponitrite and dissolve it in about 10 ml. water. Add a slight excess of silver nitrate solution, filter the flocculent precipitate on a Grade 4 sintered glass filter and wash with two 5 ml. portions of ice-cold water. Dry in a vacuum desiccator to constant weight. (Do not wash with organic solvents.)
3. What is the structure and the nature of the bonding in the hyponitrite anion?

Reference

C. C. Addison, G. A. Gamlen and R. Thompson, *J. Chem. Soc.*, **1952**, 338.

Other experiments requiring extensive use of inert-atmosphere techniques are 7.3 (Preparation of $MoCl_5$), and 11.8 (Preparation of Organic Phosphines).

Chapter 10

Non-Aqueous Solvents

Inorganic chemistry in the liquid phase has until recently been dominated by that of aqueous solutions. The main factors which have engendered this situation have been the ready availability of water and the need for more sophisticated techniques when working in non-aqueous media. Modern research has shown that a knowledge of aqueous chemistry only gives a very biased view of inorganic chemistry. Many compounds which are entirely unknown in aqueous media are readily prepared in non-aqueous solution. Anhydrous materials can also differ remarkably in structure from their hydrated forms. Severe limitations are placed upon the formation and stability of metal complexes in aqueous solution since unless their ligands are bound more strongly than would be water, hydrolysis will occur. $[Cu(NH_3)_6)]^{2+}$, for example, can only be prepared in liquid ammonia.

Non-aqueous solvents in common use include ammonia, dinitrogen tetroxide, sulphur dioxide, acetic acid, bromine trifluoride and hydrofluoric acid. Another class of solvents of great potential, and relevant to the atomic-energy industry, is that of molten salts.

It should be emphasized that non-aqueous solvents must be rigorously dry, as even traces of water can profoundly affect their properties. Thus, hydrogen fluoride is highly corrosive in the presence of water and yet the strictly anhydrous liquid is a good solvent for proteins, from which solutions they may be recovered unchanged.

SAFETY NOTE. In all experiments with inorganic non-aqueous solvents great care must be taken in handling and technique: (i) wear rubber gloves throughout; (ii) always use a good fume cupboard or a closed glass system with all vents or exhausts led to a fume cupboard; (iii) if spillages occur, destroy non-volatile solvents chemically.

References

1. L. F. Andrieth and J. Kleinberg, *Non-Aqueous Solvents*, Wiley, New York, 1953.
2. C. C. Addision, *Use of Non-Aqueous Solvents in Inorganic Chemistry*, Royal Institute of Chemistry, London, Monograph No. 2, 1960.
3. M. C. R. Symons, *Quart. Rev.*, 1959, **13**, 99.
4. W. L. Jolly, *Progr. Inorg. Chem.*, 1959, **1**, 235.

10.1 Solvent Properties of Liquid Ammonia

Liquid ammonia is probably used for preparative work more widely than any other inorganic non-aqueous solvent. It undergoes self-ionization according to the equation

$$2\,NH_3 \rightleftharpoons NH_4^+ + NH_2^-$$

For the study of reactions in liquid ammonia, the most convenient containers are transparent Dewar test-tubes of approximately 25 and 65 ml. capacity. The technique of transferring the liquid gas from a cylinder is indicated in figure 10.1; open the valve slowly. Gaseous

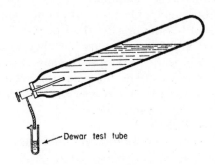

Figure 10.1. Method of transferring liquid ammonia from a cylinder to a Dewar test-tube.

ammonia may, of course, be obtained simply by using the cylinder in the normal upright position. Test-tubes of liquid ammonia should be plugged loosely with cotton wool to prevent entry of moisture.

SAFETY NOTE Wear gloves, to prevent skin burns, and safety glasses when handling liquid ammonia. Since vessels at room temperature are hot compared with the liquid gas, b.p. $-33\cdot4°c$, take care to avoid violent boiling and splashing.

Procedure

Carry out a selection of the following tests, working in pairs so as to make the best use of time.

1. Solubility of salts

Using about 10 ml. ammonia determine the approximate order of solubilities of the halides, nitrates and sulphates of (a) potassium or sodium, (b) silver, and (c) magnesium or barium.

(i) How does the solubility of the halides in ammonia compare with their solubility in water?

(ii) Compare the solubilities of nitrates and sulphates in liquid ammonia. Explain the differences.

(iii) What is the effect of anion size on the solubilities of the salts used?

2. Metathetical reactions of salts

Mix ammonia solutions of silver halide and barium or calcium nitrate. Decant the supernatant liquid, allow the precipitate to dry and warm to room temperature. Dissolve it in water and identify the ions present. Try to discover other pairs of salts which behave differently in ammonia and in water.

3. Reactions with hydrogen sulphide

Pass dry hydrogen sulphide gas into liquid ammonia. Add an ammonia solution of barium or strontium nitrate. What is the white precipitate formed and how does its stability in liquid ammonia compare with that in water? (Decant the supernatant liquid, allow the precipitate to warm to room temperature and add water.)

Repeat the above tests with a copper salt. Observe the precipitation of ammoniated copper sulphide.

4. Reaction with sodium

Add a small piece of clean sodium to liquid ammonia. Observe the blue colouration formed due to solvated electrons. Add a small crystal of a ferric salt to catalyze the formation of grey sodamide and note the consequent discharge of the blue colour. Keep this sodamide suspension for the next test.

5. Acid–base behaviour

Dissolve ammonium nitrate in ammonia and use the acid so produced (called Diver's liquid) for the following reactions.

(a) Add a little solid phenolphthalein to part of the sodamide suspension (section 4). Then *carefully* neutralize the base (NH_2^-) with the acid solution (NH_4^+).

(b) Test the solubility of the following metals in Diver's liquid: magnesium, cobalt, manganese, nickel, zinc. How does the strength of the acid, NH_4NO_3 in ammonia, compare with that of HNO_3 in water?

(c) Dissolve a little urea, guanidine or acetamide in liquid ammonia and carefully add this solution to a suspension of sodamide containing phenolphthalein. Explain your observations.

6. Reaction with organic halides

Dissolve about 0·1 g. chlorobenzene in liquid ammonia. Add small pieces of clean sodium until a permanent blue colouration is produced (about 15 min.). Neutralize excess base with a little solid ammonium nitrate, decant the supernatant liquid and allow the remaining ammonia to evaporate. Dissolve the solid residue in water and test for sodium and chloride ions. This method can be used for analysis of covalent chlorides.

7. Reducing properties of sodium solutions

Dissolve a small piece of clean sodium in ammonia and use the resulting blue solution for the following reductions. In each case add a little of the dry solid first and then add excess: (a) selenium, (b) lead or antimony, (c) a copper salt, (d) a complex cyanide, e.g., $K_2[Ni(CN)_4]$, $K_3[Fe(CN)_6]$, (e) potassium permanganate.

8. Ammonolysis

Carefully add a little phosphorus trichloride to liquid ammonia. Attempt to characterize the gas liberated and write an equation for the reaction.

10.2 Preparation of Hexa-amminechromium(III) Nitrate, $[Cr(NH_3)_6](NO_3)_3$

This compound cannot be prepared in water but is readily obtained in liquid ammonia.

Procedure

Add 0·1 g. of cleaned sodium to 35 ml. liquid ammonia in a Dewar test-tube, followed by a small crystal of a ferric salt to discharge the blue colour. When the blue colour has disappeared, add 2·5 g. anhydrous chromic chloride (prepared as in experiment 9.2) in small portions. Decant the supernatant ammonia carefully, transfer the brown residue to an evaporating basin and allow any occluded ammonia to evaporate. Dissolve the solid in 10 ml. dilute hydrochloric acid at 40°c and filter. Immediately add 4 ml. concentrated nitric acid to the filtrate and cool in ice. Filter off the resulting yellow-brown salt, wash it with cold water containing a little dilute nitric acid, then with alcohol and finally with ether. The compound is photosensitive.

Exercises

1. The solubility of hexa-amminechromium(III) nitrate in water is 2·5 g. per 100 g. water at 20°C. Calculate the solubility product and the approximate solubility in 2N nitric acid.
2. What is the function of the ferric salt in the preparation?

References

1. C. L. Rollinson and J. C. Bailar, J. Amer. Chem. Soc., 1943, 65, 250.
2. A. L. Oppegard and J. C. Bailar, Inorg. Synth., 3, 153.

10.3 Preparation of Lead Tetra-acetate, $Pb(CH_3 \cdot CO_2)_4$, and Dipyridinium Hexachloroplumbate, $(PyH)_2[PbCl_6]$

The preparation of lead tetra-acetate requires the use of acetic acid as non-aqueous solvent.

1. Lead tetra-acetate

Heat 35 ml. glacial acetic acid and 20 ml. acetic anhydride in a dry Quickfit conical flask fitted with a thermometer and a calcium chloride guard tube. When the temperature has reached 65°C, add, in two portions, 12 g. of red lead, Pb_3O_4, which has been *thoroughly dried* in an oven at 120°C. Agitate the solvent during the addition, and do not add the second portion until the first has nearly dissolved. Continue heating at 65–70°C until all the red lead has dissolved. Decant the supernatant liquid (from any residue) into a second dry flask, close with a stopper, and cool in ice-water. Crystallization should be complete in half an hour. Decant the supernatant liquid, wash the crystals with 10 ml. glacial acetic acid at 0°C, and filter rapidly. Transfer the crystals to an evaporating basin in a desiccator containing both concentrated sulphuric acid and caustic soda pellets, to remove acetic acid. Ampoule the product to prevent hydrolysis.

2. Dipyridinium hexachloroplumbate

Cool 20 ml. concentrated hydrochloric acid in ice and add 2 g. lead tetra-acetate. Add 1·5 ml. freshly distilled pyridine in 10 ml. concentrated hydrochloric acid dropwise from a burette, stirring constantly. Filter the yellow pyridinium salt on a sintered glass disc and wash twice with a few millilitres of cold concentrated hydrochloric acid. Dry in a vacuum desiccator containing both concentrated sulphuric acid and caustic soda pellets.

Exercises

1. Determine the purity of the pyridinium salt by analyzing for lead. Weigh out accurately about 0·4–0·5 g. of the pyridinium salt and dissolve it in dilute hydrochloric acid. Add excess potassium iodide solution and titrate the liberated iodine with standard sodium thiosulphate.

2. Determine, compare and discuss the relative solubilities of lead(IV) acetate and lead(II) acetate in dry ether.

3. Place 1–2 g. pyridinium hexachloroplumbate in a dry test-tube, cool in ice and slowly add a few millilitres of ice-cold concentrated sulphuric acid. Note the separation of lead tetrachloride as an oil. Remove some with a dropper and add it to water. Compare this reaction with that of stannic chloride and water. Explain any differences.

4. Discuss the structure and nature of the bonding in lead tetra-acetate and in the hexachloroplumbate anion.

5. Comment on the relative stabilities of complexes of lead(IV) and tin(IV).

References

1. K. Gutbier and H. Wissmuller, *J. prakt. Chem.*, 1914, **90**, 491.
2. O. Dimroth and R. Schweizer, *Ber.*, 1923, **56**, 1375.

10.4 Preparation of Anhydrous Copper Nitrate, $Cu(NO_3)_2$

SAFETY NOTE   This experiment must be carried out in an efficient fume cupboard.

Anhydrous copper nitrate can only be prepared in a non-aqueous medium; attempted dehydration of the hydrate, $Cu(NO_3)_2 \cdot 3H_2O$, results in decomposition of the anion. Direct reaction of copper with liquid dinitrogen tetroxide leads to the desired product.

Liquid dinitrogen tetroxide undergoes self-ionization according to the equation

$$N_2O_4 \rightleftharpoons NO^+ + NO_3^-$$

Due to the low dielectric constant ($\varepsilon = 2·4$ at 18°C) and electrical conductivity of the liquid, the equilibrium lies well to the left; consequently, ionic compounds are insoluble in it. If, however, liquid dinitrogen tetroxide is diluted with an inert solvent of high dielectric constant (e.g., nitromethane, $\varepsilon = 37$), it becomes much more reactive due to the shift of the equilibrium. Addition of ethyl acetate to the liquid greatly enhances its reactivity although the ester has a dielectric constant of only 6·02 at 25°C. Apart from its dielectric effect, ethyl acetate also acts as a donor towards the N_2O_4 molecule and the NO^+ ion:

$$(EtOAc)_n \cdot N_2O_4 \rightleftharpoons n \, EtOAc + N_2O_4 \rightleftharpoons [(EtOAc)_n \cdot NO] + NO_3^-$$

1. *Preparation of dinitrogen tetroxide, N_2O_4*

Heat dried commercial lead nitrate in a steel tube, or a glass tube containing a liner or boat. Condense the water and nitric acid evolved and pass the dinitrogen tetroxide through a phosphorus pentoxide drying tower to remove the remaining water vapour (figure 10.2).

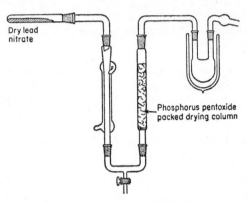

Figure 10.2. Preparation of dinitrogen tetroxide.

Condense and solidify the gas in a flask cooled to $-78\,^\circ$c and protected from the atmosphere by a phosphorus pentoxide guard tube. The solid should be colourless and the liquid, just above its melting point, pale yellow-brown. Traces of water in the liquid will produce a green colouration due to dinitrogen trioxide.

2. *Preparation of copper nitrate, $Cu(NO_3)_2$*

Clean 10 g. of copper sheet with an abrasive cloth, wash it with water and acetone and dry well. Transfer to a large oven-dried Quickfit test-tube (B24 or larger), closed by a phosphorus pentoxide guard tube. Introduce 20 ml. dry ethyl acetate, cool in ice, and add 20 ml. dinitrogen tetroxide. Allow the mixture to warm slowly to room temperature. When reaction is complete – several hours or over-night – remove any unreacted copper, re-cool in ice, and add a fur-ther quantity of dinitrogen tetroxide *slowly* until no more blue $Cu(NO_3)_2 \cdot N_2O_4$ is precipitated. Keep the tube closed with the guard tube whenever possible. Separate the blue solid in a dried filter tube containing a coarse sintered glass disc (figure 10.3). Wash with dinitrogen tetroxide and transfer to a subliming vessel on the general-purpose vacuum line. Pump off occluded dinitrogen tetroxide at room temperature and decompose the adduct by raising the

temperature to 120°C using an oil bath. With solid carbon dioxide–
acetone coolant in the cold finger of the sublimer, bring the oil bath
to 200°C.

SAFETY NOTE   Condense the evolved N_2O_4 in a small trap
and, at the end of the experiment, allow it to warm up in a
fume cupboard.

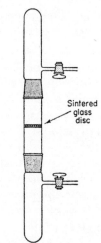

Figure 10.3. Filter tube.

When sublimation of the anhydrous copper nitrate is complete, admit
dry air to the vacuum line and remove the product to a dry-box.
Hydration is immediate in the presence of moisture. Ampoule the
product.

Exercises

1. Analyze for copper by precipitation and weighing as [Cu(en)₂][HgI₄].
2. Enumerate and explain the differences between hydrated and anhydrous
copper nitrate. What is the structure of each (include the gas phase)?

Reference

1. C. C. Addison and B. J. Hathaway, *J. Chem. Soc.*, **1958**, 3099.
2. N. Logan, W. B. Simpson and S. C. Wallwork, *Proc. Chem. Soc.*, 1964, 341.

10.5 Preparation of Iodine Monochloride and Iodine
Trichloride and Some Adducts of the Form (R → I)⁺Cl⁻

The interhalogens ICl and ICl₃ are readily prepared. Iodine is much
more electropositive than chlorine and has a comparatively low
ionization potential. Groups with electron-donating properties (e.g.,

pyridine) stabilize the iodine cation, forming adducts of the type $(R \rightarrow I)^{+}Cl^{-}$. Iodine monochloride is a self-ionizing non-aqueous solvent.

$$2 \, ICl \rightleftharpoons I^{+} + ICl_2^{-}$$

1. *Preparation of iodine monochloride*

Condense approximately 10 ml. liquid chlorine into an accurately weighed dry boiling tube (with a ground-glass stopper) cooled to $-78°c$. Add approximately 25 g. iodine, accurately weighed, and allow the contents of the tube to warm slowly to room temperature, whereupon uncombined chlorine will boil off. Reweigh the tube and calculate the weight of chlorine combined with iodine. From this weight, deduce the amount of iodine needed to make the stoicheiometry 1 : 1. Add the required amount of iodine, stopper and warm gently until a dark liquid is formed. Allow the product to stand overnight. Purify the iodine chloride by melting and allowing it to cool slowly until 80% solidifies. Decant the supernatant liquid. Repeat this procedure twice and ampoule the product, which should melt at $27\cdot2°c$. Iodine monochloride is very corrosive towards skin, cork or rubber, and any spills should immediately be treated with dilute hydrochloric acid.

2. *Preparation of iodine trichloride*

Condense approximately 10 ml. liquid chlorine into a dry boiling tube cooled to $-78°c$. Add 12 g. powdered iodine very slowly to give a flocculent orange-yellow powder – iodine trichloride. Evaporate excess chlorine by allowing the temperature to rise slowly. Immediately seal the product in tared ampoules.

3. *Preparation of adducts of ICl of the form $R \rightarrow ICl$*

Dissolve 2 ml. redistilled pyridine in 10 ml. dry carbon tetrachloride contained in a two-neck 250 ml. flask. Dissolve 4 g. iodine monochloride in 50 ml. dry carbon tetrachloride and add dropwise from a separating funnel to the pyridine solution. Stir the resulting solution vigorously. Filter off the yellow solid so formed; wash with carbon tetrachloride and dry in air. Recrystallize the adduct from ethanol, wash with carbon tetrachloride and dry in air.

Other adducts of the form $R \cdot ICl$ may be prepared similarly from organic bases such as quinoline, isoquinoline, pyrrole and acetamide.

Exercises

1. Record the infrared spectrum of the adduct and compare it with that of the pure base. Explain differences.

2. Bearing in mind the products of the self-ionization of iodine monochloride, describe what reactions you would expect between it and (a) $AlCl_3$, (b) concentrated HCl, (c) KCl.

3. Why is I^+ stabilized by pyridine whereas the analagous piperidine adduct is very unstable?

4. Analyze iodine monochloride for iodine. How would you also analyze it for chlorine?

References

1. J. Cornog and R. A. Karges, *Inorg. Synth.*, **1**, 165.
2. G. B. Kauffman and K. L. Stevens, *Ibid*, **7**, 176.

Element-Organic Chemistry

I. π-COMPLEXES OF TRANSITION METALS

11.1 Preparation of Ferrocene, $Fe(\pi\text{-}C_5H_5)_2$

Of the several methods available for the synthesis of ferrocene (see *Quart. Rev.*, 1959, **9**, 391) that using diethylamine is the simplest, although not of very general application.

$$FeCl_3 + Fe \rightarrow FeCl_2$$
$$FeCl_2 + C_5H_6 + 2\ Et_2NH \rightarrow Fe(\pi\text{-}C_5H_5)_2 + 2\ Et_2NH \cdot HCl$$

Procedure

A 250 ml. three-neck flask fitted with a stirrer, reflux condenser and inlet for admission of nitrogen, and a stopper in the third neck, is charged with 100 ml. dry tetrahydrofuran (Appendix 3). Add, with stirring, 27·1 g. anhydrous ferric chloride followed by 4·7 g. iron powder (preferably 300 mesh). Heat with stirring under nitrogen at the reflux temperature for 4·5 hr., to give a grey powder and a brown supernatant liquid.

Meanwhile, prepare cyclopentadiene (b.p. 40°c) as follows. Distil commercial dicyclopentadiene using a short column (3/4 in. diam. × 8–12 in. length) filled with glass helices. The distilled cyclopentadiene should be kept at dry-ice temperature until used.

When the ferrous chloride solution has been refluxed, remove the THF under reduced pressure until the residue is almost dry. Cool the flask in an ice bath and add 42 ml. cyclopentadiene and 100 ml. diethylamine. Stir the mixture vigorously at room temperature for 6–8 hr. or overnight. Remove excess amine under reduced pressure and extract the residue repeatedly with refluxing petroleum ether. Filter hot and evaporate the solvent to leave ferrocene. Recrystallize from cyclohexane. Record yield and melting point.

Exercises

1. Record the infrared spectrum of ferrocene using both 'Nujol' and hexa-chlorbutadiene (or 'Fluorlube') mulls. (Rather thick mulls will be necessary.) Assign the observed bands to their associated ring modes. (See *J. Chem. Phys.*, 1953, **21**, 1307.) Examine a copy of the proton NMR spectrum.

2. Investigate the reaction of ferrocene with (a) dilute nitric acid; (b) a benzene solution of benzoquinone and picric acid; (c) aqueous silver nitrate followed by potassium iodide–iodine solution.

Reference

The preparative method is that of G. Wilkinson, *Org. Synth*, Collective Vol. IV, p. 476.

11.2 Preparation of Nickelocene, $Ni(\pi\text{-}C_5H_5)_2$ *

Dissolve 30 g. hydrated nickel chloride, $NiCl_2 \cdot 6 H_2O$, in 60 ml. water. Filter, warm to 60°C and add *gradually* 100 ml. 0·880 ammonia. Allow the solution to cool slowly to room temperature; then cool in ice-water, when violet crystals will be deposited. Filter at the pump and wash with ice-water, ethanol and then ether. Suck dry at the pump. Record the yield of $[Ni(NH_3)_6]VCl_2$.

Prepare a solution of 12 g. cyclopentadiene monomer (see experiment 11.1) in 100 ml. pure dry THF (Appendix 3) in a 250 ml. three-neck flask fitted with a stirrer, reflux condenser and means of sweeping with nitrogen. Stopper the third neck and reserve it for addition of solids. Flush the apparatus with dry nitrogen and dissolve 3 g. sodium wire in the solution. Cool to 30°C after dissolution of the sodium and add 21 g. $[Ni(NH_3)_6]Cl_2$. Warm the mixture gently to 35–40°C, when the reaction proceeds smoothly with evolution of gas. Complete the reaction by heating at 65°C for 2 hr. Remove the solvent by distillation and transfer the dry residue to a sublimation apparatus (figure 11.1) in a dry-bag (oxygen-free). Evacuate on a vacuum line and heat to about 80°C with an oil bath, when dark green nickelocene (m.p. 172°C) sublimes. Ampoule the product in a dry-bag. Record the yield.

Exercises

1. Bis(cyclopentadienyl) nickel(III) cation (yellow-orange in aqueous solution) may be obtained from nickelocene in several ways. Carry out the following:

(a) Mix ether solutions of nickelocene and picric acid. Bubble air through and isolate the resulting black bis(cyclopentadienyl) nickel(III) picrate.

(b) Extract an ether solution of nickelocene with dilute nitric acid. Add potassium iodide–iodine solution.

2. Determine the magnetic moment of nickelocene. Discuss the result and suggest a bonding scheme.

* Cobaltocene may be prepared similarly. Prepare the hexa–ammine on 3x scale and use an oxygen-free atmosphere throughout.

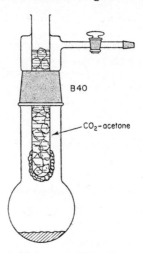

Figure 11.1. Vacuum sublimation apparatus.

Reference

G. Wilkinson, P. L. Pauson and F. A. Cotton, *J. Amer. Chem. Soc.*, 1954, **76**, 1970.

11.3 Preparation of Bis(π-cyclopentadienyl)titanium(IV)-dichloride, [TiCl$_2$(π-C$_5$H$_5$)$_2$]

$$2\ NaC_5H_5 + TiCl_4 \rightarrow [TiCl_2(\pi\text{-}C_5H_5)_2] + 2\ NaCl$$

Using the apparatus of experiment 11·1 and working under nitrogen, add 1·5 g. sodium wire to 75 ml. pure dry THF (Appendix 3). Then add dropwise 4·5 g. freshly prepared cyclopentadiene monomer (see experiment 11.1) and stir the solution until all gas has evolved. Cool in ice, transfer to a dropping funnel, and run slowly into an ice-cold solution of 5 g. titanium tetrachloride in 50 ml. pure THF. Stir the solution rapidly for a further 3 hr. at room temperature and then remove the solvent under reduced pressure, firstly at the water pump and secondly on a vacuum line.

Transfer the dry residue to a thimble and extract repeatedly with chloroform in a Soxhlet apparatus through which a slow stream of hydrogen chloride is passed (see figure 11.2 and *Inorg. Synth.*, 1, 147). When extraction is complete, distil off chloroform to low bulk and cool the remaining solution. Filter off the red crystal plates which separate and recrystallize from toluene. Dry in air. A further crop of crystals may be obtained from the mother liquor by further evaporation.

Exercises

1. Hydrolyze a portion of the product by boiling with alkali and determine the chloride content.
2. Record and discuss the infrared spectrum.
3. How would you prepare: (a) $Ti(\pi\text{-}C_5H_5)_3$; (b) $[Ti(CO)_2(\pi\text{-}C_5H_5)_2]$?
4. Discuss the nature of the bonding of the ring to the metal.

References

1. G. Wilkinson and J. M. Birmingham, *J. Amer. Chem. Soc.*, 1954, **76**, 4281.
2. M. A. Bennett, *et al.*, *Nature*, 1964, **201**, 1318.

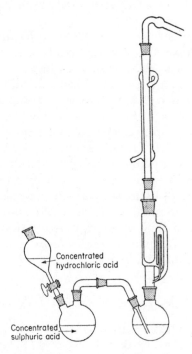

Figure 11.2. Apparatus for the extraction of bis(π-cyclopenta-dienyl)titanium(IV) dichloride.

11.4 Cobalticinium Salts, $[Co(\pi\text{-}C_5H_5)_2]^+A^-$

The cobalticinium ion, $[Co(\pi\text{-}C_5H_5)_2]^+$, is iso-electronic with ferrocene. It is more stable than ferrocene and is not attacked by aqua regia, alkaline hydrogen peroxide or ozone in acetic acid, but it is attacked by fusion with bisulphate and by fuming perchloric acid.

The salts (of colourless anions) are yellow, diamagnetic and have precipitation reactions similar to those of the caesium ion. Thus $[Co(\pi\text{-}C_5H_5)_2]OH$ is a strong base which absorbs carbon dioxide from the air.

Procedure

$$2\ NaC_5H_5 + CoCl_2 \rightarrow Co(\pi\text{-}C_5H_5)_2 + 2\ NaCl$$

$$Co(\pi\text{-}C_5H_5)_2 \xrightarrow{[0]} [Co(\pi\text{-}C_5H_5)_2]^+ \xrightarrow{I_3^-} [Co(\pi\text{-}C_5H_5)_2]I_3$$

(i) Prepare anhydrous cobalt(II) chloride from the hexahydrate by the method of experiment 9.2.

(ii) Prepare about 300 ml. pure THF (Appendix 3). Use a small portion of this to wash 5 g. of freshly made sodium wire.

(iii) Fit a three-neck flask with a nitrogen inlet, stirrer, reflux condenser and dropping funnel. Flush the apparatus with dry nitrogen for 20 min. and then introduce 5 g. sodium wire and 80 ml. fresh THF into the flask. Stir and slowly add from the funnel a solution of 25 ml. cyclopentadiene monomer (prepared as in experiment 11.1) in 80 ml. THF, taking about half an hour. Stir for 2 hr. and then add 14 g. anhydrous cobalt(II) chloride. Stir for a further 2 hr., then add sufficient methanol to destroy any residual sodium. Add a few millilitres of hydrogen peroxide and pass air through the solution for about 15 min. to form a dark-brown solution. The cobalticinium ion can then be precipitated with aqueous potassium tri-iodide solution, forming a dark-brown sludge. Filter, wash liberally with water and dry *in vacuo*.

Exercises

1. Record the infrared spectrum of the product and compare it with that of ferrocene.
2. What happens when $[CO(\pi\text{-}C_5H_5)_2]^+$ is treated with (a) LiAlH₄, followed, when reduction is complete, by (b) CCl₄, followed by (c) CF₃I?

References

1. G. Wilkinson, *J. Amer. Chem. Soc.*, 1952, **74**, 6148.
2. M. L. H. Green, L. Pratt and G. Wilkinson, *J. Chem. Soc.*, **1959**, 3753.
3. G. E. Coates, *Organometallic Compounds*, 2nd edition, Methuen, London, 1960, p. 302.

11.5 π-Complexes of Molybdenum

Molybdenum hexacarbonyl, Mo(CO)₆, is easily substituted by a wide variety of neutral ligands (see, for example, F. A. Cotton and

G. Wilkinson, *Advanced Inorganic Chemistry*, Interscience, 1962, p. 615) which can form σ- and π-bonds with the metal atom. Thus chelating diphosphines or diarsines react to give compounds of the types [Mo(CO)₄(diphos.)] and [Mo(CO)₂(diphos.)₂], whereas olefins and certain ring systems form π-complexes. The following preparations require only easily available ligands. Diphosphines and diarsines cannot be purchased and their preparation is lengthy.

SAFETY NOTE The solid molybdenum hexacarbonyl is appreciably volatile and very toxic. Handle it only in a fume cupboard and avoid spillages. Weigh in a stoppered tube.

1. *Preparation of 2,2,1-bicycloheptadienemolybdenum tetracarbonyl, [Mo(CO)₄(diolefin)]*

Reflux 2·5 g. molybdenum hexacarbonyl with 4 ml. 2,2,1-bicycloheptadiene in 20 ml. petroleum ether (b.p. 100–120°c), under nitrogen, for 20 hr. Remove the solvent by evacuation and extract the solid residue with 10 ml. portions of petroleum ether (b.p. 40–60°c). Filter and cool the extract to −78°c, when pale yellow crystals separate. Transfer the crystals to a tared ampoule and remove last traces of the solvent on the vacuum line. (Place the whole ampoule inside a suitable container on the vacuum line.) Remove and quickly seal the ampoule. Record the yield and determine the melting point of a small specimen.

NOTE 1. The olefin should be freshly distilled before use. Handle it only *in a fume cupboard.*
2. All petroleum ether used in the experiment should be sodium-dried.

Reference

M. A. Bennett, L. Pratt and G. Wilkinson, *J. Chem. Soc.*, **1961**, 2043.

2. *Preparation of (π-N-methylpyridinemolybdenum tricarbonyl), (Mo(CO)₃(π-C₅H₄NMe)]*

Prepare N-methylpyridinium iodide by reacting equimolar quantities of pyridine and methyl iodide. Recrystallize from acetone, wash in sodium-dried ether and dry in a vacuum desiccator.

Reflux a mixture of 2 g. molybdenum hexacarbonyl and 3 g. N-methylpyridinium iodide in 40 ml. THF (purified as in Appendix 3) for $3\frac{1}{2}$ hr. under nitrogen. Remove solvent by evacuation, using a splash head. Working rapidly extract the solid residue with small portions of ethanol–petroleum ether, filter and cool to $-78°$c. Dry the crystals on the vacuum line as above.

Gentle heating causes loss of carbon monoxide and formation of the required product.

Exercises

1. Draw the structures of both products. What would happen if pyridine was used for the second preparation instead of N-methylpyridinium iodide?
2. Record the infrared spectra of both products. Relate the carbonyl stretching frequencies to the molecular and electronic structures involved and show why they are lower than the stretching frequency of carbon monoxide. Identify two bands characteristic of the pyridine ring.

Reference

1. E. O. Fischer and K. Ofele, *Z. Naturforsch.*, 1959, **14b**, 736.
2. E. W. Abel, M. A. Bennett and G. Wilkinson, *J. Chem. Soc.*, **1959**, 2323.

II. REACTIONS WITH PHENYL-LITHIUM

Organolithium compounds are of considerable importance in synthetic work due to their high reactivity, simple preparation and ready solubility in inert solvents. They are mainly used for the same sort of syntheses as Grignard reagents but often confer advantages such as greater reactivity or ease of working up. It is usual to prepare and use an organolithium reagent *in situ*, rather than isolate it. The subject has been excellently reviewed by G. E. Coates in his *Organometallic Compounds*, Methuen, London, 1960.

Organolithium reagents readily react with a variety of covalent halides, such as those of boron, tin, phosphorus, arsenic and antimony.

Preparation of a phenyl-lithium suspension

$$2\,\text{Li} + \text{RX} \rightarrow \text{RLi} + \text{LiX}$$

Lithium metal is generally supplied as rather large, hard lumps. Cut off and weigh a suitable lump and hammer it into a thin sheet. Scrape it free of its adherent layer of oxide, etc., under hexane and then cut it into small pieces with scissors. Allow the pieces to fall into the solvent to be used for the reaction.

A slight excess (about 5%) of RX should in general be used. Prepare 3 g. lithium as above and drop into 100 ml. sodium-dried ether contained in a three-neck flask fitted with stirrer, condenser and dropping funnel. This reaction should be carried out in an atmosphere of dry nitrogen. Place a solution of 35·5 g. bromobenzene in 75 ml. ether in the funnel and add it slowly, with moderate stirring, so as to maintain a steady reflux of ether. Continue until nearly all the lithium has dissolved.

Gilman's colour test I

Reactions using organolithium reagents are sometimes rather slow and a qualitative test for completion is therefore necessary. Three tests for different groups of organometallic compound have been devised by Gilman but we are concerned only with the first. It detects any organometallic compound (not necessarily a lithium compound) sufficiently reactive to add to an aryl ketone.

Using a drawn-out dropper which has been flushed with dry nitrogen, withdraw about 1 ml. reaction mixture and add it to 1 ml. of a 1% solution of Michler's Ketone (4,4'-tetramethyldiaminobenzophenone) in benzene. Add a little water to hydrolyze the reaction product and then oxidize it by the addition of a 0·2% solution of iodine in glacial acetic acid. A blue to green colour indicates the presence of phenyl–lithium. (Write out the reaction scheme.) If the reaction mixture under test contains a product which reacts with iodine, a correspondingly larger amount of the latter will need to be added.

11.6 Preparation of some Phenyl-Tin Compounds

Prepare Ph$_3$SnLi as below and use it to carry out the subsequent reactions, working under dry nitrogen.

1. Triphenylstannyl-lithium, Ph$_3$SnLi

Prepare a suspension of 8·5 g. finely ground anhydrous stannous chloride in 50 ml. ether and cool to −10°c. Stir well and add, dropwise, 0·135 mole (three equivalents) of phenyl-lithium in 137 ml. ether. The colour of the reaction mixture will change through orange to deep red and finally to light tan. Use colour test I for completion.

2. *Hexaphenyldistannane, $Ph_3Sn \cdot SnPh_3$*

To 0·008 mole Ph_3SnLi add 3 g. Ph_3SnCl* dissolved in 80 ml. ether. Reflux for 1½ hr. and hydrolyze by pouring into a saturated aqueous solution of ammonium chloride. The white solid obtained should be combined with a further quantity which will be the solid residue from the ether layer. Recrystallize from excess petroleum ether (b.p. 80–120°c). Determine the m.p. (230°c).

3. *Tetraphenyl-tin, Ph_4Sn, and triphenylethyl–tin, Ph_3SnEt*

Add 0·038 mole ethyl iodide dissolved in 35 ml. ether to 0·035 mole Ph_3SnLi. Reflux for 1½ hr. and hydrolyze as in section 2. Recrystallize the yellow solid from petroleum ether to obtain pure tetraphenyl-tin, m.p. 224–225°c. The ether layer will deposit a deep-yellow solid which should be extracted with 80 ml. petroleum ether (b.p. 60–80°c). Cool in ice and recrystallize the yellow Ph_3SnEt so obtained from a minimum of ethanol. mp. 56–58°c.

Exercises

1. Write out the reaction scheme for the formation of each tin compound prepared.
2. Record the infrared spectrum of Ph_3SnEt in 'Nujol' and in HCB (or 'Fluorlube') and identify bands characteristic of the ethyl group.
3. How does Ph_3SnLi react with (a) carbon dioxide, (b) benzophenone, and (c) ethylene oxide ?
4. Devise a scheme for the synthesis of Me_2EtSnI.

References

1. H. Gilman and S. D. Rosenberg, *J. Amer. Chem. Soc.*, 1952, **74**, 531.
2. H. Gilman and S. D. Rosenberg, *J. Org. Chem.*, 1953, **18**, 680; 1554.

11.7 Studies in the Chemistry of Phenyl-Antimony Compounds

Carry out one of the following preparations.

1. *Triphenyl-antimony, Ph_3Sb*

Prepare phenyl-lithium in ether as described above. Then add dropwise whilst stirring a solution of 13·5 g. antimony trichloride in 75 ml. ether, adjusting the rate of addition so as to keep the ether at steady reflux. Use Gilman's colour test I at intervals, beginning when about half the antimony trichloride has been added. It is important not to

* Available commercially.

add excess antimony trichloride as the following disproportionation takes place:

$$Ph_3Sb + SbCl_3 \rightleftharpoons Ph_2SbCl + PhSbCl_2$$

When all the phenyl-lithium has reacted, continue stirring for a further 40 min. and then remove any unreacted lithium. Pour the contents of the flask into an equal volume of ice-water and shake. Take off the ether layer, leaving suspended matter at the interface with the aqueous layer. Extract the aqueous layer twice with 70 ml. portions of ether.

Evaporate the combined ether solutions to dryness and recrystallize the pale-yellow product from 25 ml. petroleum ether (40–60°c) with charcoal. Concentrate the solution to obtain a further batch of crystals, m.p. 48–50°c.

Exercises

1. Investigate the effect of (a) chlorine, (b) iodine on Ph_3Sb. Purify any product you obtain and try to elucidate its structure.
2. Attempt, on a small scale, to nitrate Ph_3Sb with a mixture of concentrated nitric and sulphuric acids. Take the infrared spectrum of the product and deduce as much as you can about its structure.

2. *Pentaphenyl-antimony, Ph_5Sb*

Prepare phenyl-lithium as above. Withdraw 30–35 ml. of the suspension and reserve it for exercise 1 below. Now prepare a suspension of 0·04 mole antimony pentachloride (if a new ampoule must be opened, do this under supervision, following the method of Appendix 2) in dry ether which has been cooled to −70°c in a flask protected with a phosphorus pentoxide tube. Transfer the suspension to the dropping funnel and follow the procedure for triphenyl-antimony.

After separation and extraction, combine the ether solutions and strip off the ether. Recrystallize the product from acetonitrile. m.p. 168–170°c.

Exercises

1. Treat a calculated quantity of pentaphenyl-antimony with the 30–35 ml. phenyl-lithium solution reserved above. Work up and isolate any product. What is it?
2. React a sample of pentaphenyl-antimony with an equimolar quantity of iodine at 40°c. Isolate any product formed, determine its m.p. and analyze for iodine. What can you deduce about its structure?
3. Does the reaction of pentaphenyl-antimony and chlorine lead to similar products to those of exercise 2?

References
1. G. Wittig and K. Clauss, *Annalen*, 1952, **577**, 26 (or *Chem. Abs.*, 1953, **47**, 3261b).
2. G. E. Coates, *Organometallic Compounds*, Methuen, London, 1960.
3. P. I. Wheatley and G. Wittig, *Proc. Chem. Soc.*, 1962, 251.

III. σ- AND π-BONDED COMPLEXES

11.8 Preparation of an Organic Phosphine and its Complex with Nickel Chloride

Organic phosphines and arsines are amongst the most valuable types of ligand available for metal-complex chemistry. Mono- and bidentate types are in common use whilst tri- and tetra-dentate ligands are occasionally employed, being particularly useful for forcing an unusual stereochemistry on a metal atom in a given valence state, e.g., the tetra-arsine, tris(o-diphenylarsinophenyl)arsine, can be used to make five-coordinate platinum(II) (*Proc. Chem. Soc.*, 1961, 170). In this experiment you prepare an organic phosphine and use it to form a complex. Phosphines are unstable to oxygen and all operations should therefore be carried out under nitrogen. Organic phosphines may be destroyed by an oxidizing agent such as bromine water.

> SAFETY NOTE Phosphines have a penetrating and unpleasant odour and are poisonous. The vapour can be smelt in very low concentration and this acts as an excellent indicator of the effectiveness of the safety precautions. Clearly, the whole process must be carried out in an efficient fume cupboard. When handling the liquid product, wear rubber gloves and wash them immediately you have finished the experiment as liquid phosphines are contact-poisons.

Choice of conditions

The best yields of phosphines are obtained if the entire preparation is carried out under nitrogen. This is a somewhat cumbersome business and requires the construction of a certain amount of non-standard glassware. Many of the commonly used phosphines (PPr_3^n, PBu_3^n, $PPhEt_2$, for example) are sufficiently insensitive to oxygen that they can be handled quickly in air, or under a blanket of nitrogen.

We describe here a general procedure for the preparation of

phenyldiethylphosphine, $PPhEt_2$, entirely under nitrogen, on a two-litre-flask scale. Using this procedure two to three working days are required for the preparation of approximately 80 g. of pure product. This may be too long for many teaching purposes. By cutting the scale down to (say) 500 ml. and carrying out all the transfer operations in standard apparatus flushed as far as possible with nitrogen, considerable speeding up may be effected. Indeed, the crude product may be used directly for the formation of complexes. The demonstrator will decide what level of sophistication is required. The same general procedure may be used for the preparation of other monophosphines.

Procedure

$$\text{Mg} + \text{EtBr} \rightarrow \text{EtMgBr} \xrightarrow{\text{PPhCl}_2} \text{PPhEt}_2$$

(i) Assemble the apparatus of figure 11.3; lubricate the joints with silicone grease. Charge the flask with 31·7 g. magnesium turnings. Pass a fast stream of nitrogen through the apparatus for about 20 min. whilst rotating the stirrer at a moderate speed (N.B. a mechanically sealed stirrer gland should be used, not a mercury-sealed type, as the apparatus will be subjected to some pressure). Then reduce the flow and maintain at about one bubble per second throughout the preparation. Run in 200 ml. ether and then about 1 ml. ethyl bromide. Drop a few crystals of iodine into the local concentration of bromide and warm the flask with the heat of the hand. When the colour of iodine begins to be discharged, start the stirrer and add 99 ml. ethyl bromide dissolved in 150 ml. ether over half an hour. Keep the temperature at 25–30°c by slight cooling from a solid carbon dioxide–acetone bath. Add 200 ml. ether. The mixture may be left overnight at this point if desired, provided slow stirring and passage of nitrogen is continued.

Cool the reaction mixture to −45°c and stir vigorously. Add 80 ml. commercial phenyldichlorophosphine, $PPhCl_2$,* in 200 ml. ether dropwise over half an hour. During the addition the mixture becomes much more viscous and a white solid separates. This must be kept from settling on the sides of the flask by vigorous stirring and by applying the least cooling necessary to keep the temperature at −45°c. When addition is complete, allow the mixture to warm to 0°c.

(ii) Hydrolyze by addition of 280 g. ammonium chloride in 1080 ml. oxygen-free water (boil out under nitrogen), beginning slowly and adding the last 400 ml. as rapidly as possible. Stir throughout and

* Available commercially.

maintain a fast stream of nitrogen. Warm to 25°c and then stop the stirrer. Syphon the ether layer into the filtering apparatus as follows. Remove the thermometer from the flask and insert the syphon tube against a fast flow of nitrogen. Close the nitrogen by-pass on the outlet side of the flask, thereby forcing the ether layer into the filter

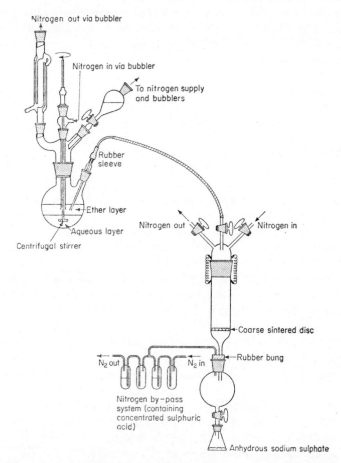

Figure 11.3. Apparatus for the preparation of organic phosphines.

apparatus, which has been previously flushed with nitrogen. Wash the aqueous layer with two portions of 100 ml. ether and syphon over. Take off any aqueous layer that may have come over and then run the ether solution into two one-litre conical flasks, each containing 100 g. anhydrous sodium sulphate and flushed with nitrogen prior to filling. Close the flasks with rubber bungs and seal with adhesive tape. Stand overnight.

(iii) Meanwhile, assemble the apparatus of figure 11.4 and drop a few chips of porcelain into the flask. Lag the Vigreux column with cotton-wool before fitting the large dropping funnel. Prepare a nitrogen capillary leak and check that it fits into the distilling flask: store it in a safe place. Flush the entire apparatus with a fast stream of nitrogen for about ¾ hr., close off, and leave overnight.

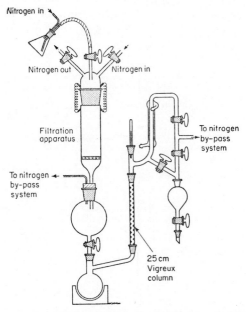

Figure 11.4. Apparatus for the filtration and distillation of organic phosphines.

Transfer the dry phosphine–ether solution from the flasks to the filter apparatus by quickly attaching to the delivery tube and pressurizing with nitrogen. Wash each flask with small amounts of ether. Adjust nitrogen flows and then distil off the ether at a steady rate at atmospheric pressure using an oil bath.

Pass a fast stream of nitrogen through the nitrogen by-pass attached to the take-off head and remove the large dropping funnel. Quickly insert the nitrogen capillary leak. Adjust nitrogen flows so that gas is passed in via the leak and evacuate the apparatus by means of a water pump. Vacuum should be applied carefully as ether dissolved in the crude phosphine will froth considerably. Raise the temperature of the oil bath and slowly distil the phosphine. Discard the first 2 or 3 ml. and collect the remainder in the receiver. Close the tap leading to the vacuum pump and bring the apparatus to room pressure by admitting nitrogen to the take-off head via the by-pass tap.

Ampoule the product under nitrogen (tared ampoules) using the apparatus of figure 11.5.

Cleaning of apparatus.

Wipe all ground-glass joints with cotton-wool lubricated with chloroform. Rinse successively with chloroform, acetone, water, bromine water, water (twice more) and finally with ethanol and acetone.

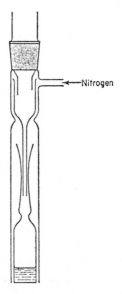

Figure 11.5. Apparatus for ampouling liquids under nitrogen.

(iv) *Dichlorobis(phenyldiethylphosphine)nickel*(II), [*NiCl₂*(*PPhEt₂*)₂]

(iv) *Dichlorobis(phenyldiethylphosphine)nickel*(II), $[NiCl_2(PPhEt_2)_2]$

Select an ampoule containing about $\frac{1}{2}$–1 ml. phosphine. Working under nitrogen as far as possible, add the contents of the ampoule to a calculated amount of a saturated solution of nickelous chloride in 50 % ethanol–water. Recrystallize the complex from ethanol.

Exercises

1. List the possible isomers of the complex. What methods would you use to decide which is produced? Which isomer is your complex?

2. Discuss the importance of $d\pi$–$d\pi$ bonding in the complex.

References

1. W. C. Davies, *et al.*, *J. Chem. Soc.*, **1929**, 33; 1262.
2. W. J. C. Dyke, W. C. Davies and W. J. Jones, *Ibid.*, **1930**, 463.

Chapter 12

Electrolytic Preparations

Oxidation or reduction by electrolytic means sometimes provides an attractive method of preparation of compounds in which a central atom has either a rather high or a rather low oxidation state. The preparations given below are typical of the use of electrolytic synthesis. Apart from peroxosulphates, oxidizing agents such as chlorates, perchlorates and silver(II) oxide are readily made. Reduction to the metallic state (including the formation of amalgams) and the preparation of compounds of transition metals in low oxidation states (e.g., $Ti^{(III)}$, $V^{(III)}$, $Cr^{(II)}$) are the most frequent applications of cathodic reduction. It is hardly necessary to stress the industrial importance of electrolytic processes.

From Faraday's laws of electrolysis, the *theoretical yield* of a cell reaction is given by

$$\frac{I \cdot t}{96,500} \times \text{(Gram equivalent wt. of product)}$$

In practice, a slightly lower yield is obtained. A term sometimes used to express the percentage yield of an electrolytic synthesis is

$$\text{Current efficiency} = \frac{\text{Actual yield} \times 100}{\text{Theoretical yield}}$$

Power for electrolytic experiments may be, conveniently, either (a) a bank of high-capacity storage batteries or (b) rectified a.c.

12.1 Preparation and Reactions of Peroxosalts of Sulphur

1. *Potassium peroxodisulphate, $K_2S_2O_8$*

$$2 SO_4^{2-} \rightarrow S_2O_8^{2-} + 2 e^-$$

The cell for this preparation (figure 12.1) is simply a boiling tube into which is inserted the electrode assembly. The anode is 1 cm. of 22 gauge platinum wire sealed into a glass tube around which is wound the platinum wire cathode. The anode current density should be about 1 amp/cm.^{2}.

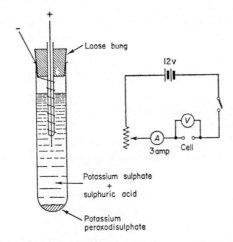

Figure 12.1. Cell and circuit for the preparation of potassium peroxodisulphate.

Fill the boiling tube with a solution of 19·6 ml. concentrated sulphuric acid in 50 ml. water and saturate at 0°c with potassium sulphate. Immerse the tube in ice and switch on the current. After about 45 min., collect the crystals which have fallen from the anode and wash them successively with alcohol and ether. Resaturate the filtrate with potassium sulphate and repeat the run several times to obtain sufficient material for the remainder of the experiment. Work out the current efficiency of the process.

Reactions of potassium peroxodisulphate. Examine the effect of the following reagents on a saturated solution of potassium peroxodisulphate and explain your observations. In each case, compare the reaction with that of hydrogen peroxide.

(a) Acidified potassium iodide solution; warm gently. Could this be made the basis of a volumetric determination of peroxodisulphates?

(b) Silver nitrate solution.

(c) Manganous sulphate in dilute sulphuric acid to which has been added one drop of silver nitrate solution.

(d) Titanic sulphate solution.

2. *Peroxosulphuric acid, H_2SO_5*

Triturate 1 g. potassium peroxodisulphate with 2 g. concentrated sulphuric acid cooled in ice. Allow to stand for 1 hr. and then pour onto crushed ice. Precipitate excess sulphuric acid by addition of barium hydrogen phosphate (made from 1 : 1 barium hydroxide and phosphoric acid) and filter on a sintered glass crucible. Draw a current of air through the filtrate to remove dissolved ozone; the resulting solution contains about 15% peroxosulphuric acid.

Reactions of peroxosulphuric acid. Examine the effects of the following reagents on solutions of peroxosulphuric acid and explain your observations.

(a) Concentrated hydrochloric acid.

(b) Hydrobromic acid.

(c) Acidified potassium iodide solution (cold).

(d) A few crystals of copper sulphate followed by caustic soda solution.

Differences between peroxosulphates and peroxodisulphates. Investigate the effects of the following reagents:

(a) aniline,

(b) a 2% alcoholic benzidine solution.

3. *Tetrapyridinesilver(II) peroxodisulphate, $[Ag(py)_4]S_2O_8$*

Pour a mixture of 12 ml. 5% aqueous silver nitrate and 5 ml. freshly distilled pyridine into a well stirred solution of potassium peroxodisulphate (7·5 g. in 500 ml.). Allow the solution to stand for 30 min. and then filter off the yellow crystalline product. Wash with water and dry in a desiccator over potassium hydroxide pellets.

Exercises

1. Discuss the steric and electronic structures of the peroxodisulphate and peroxosulphate anions.

2. Why is the stability of Ag^{2+} increased by coordination with pyridine? What other ligands might be used in place of pyridine?

Reference

Walton, *Inorganic Preparations.*

12.2 Preparation of Potassium Pentachloroaquomolybdate(III), $K_2[MoCl_5(H_2O)]$

$$MoO_3 + 6\,H^+ + 6\,Cl^- + 3\,e^- \rightarrow [MoCl_6]^{3-} + 3\,H_2O$$

$$[MoCl_6]^{3-} + H_2O \rightarrow [MoCl_5(H_2O)]^{2-} + Cl^-$$

As indicated by the reaction scheme, the following preparation produces two main products, both containing $Mo^{(III)}$. The combined yields are low and there is little doubt that the electrolytically reduced solution contains a complex mixture of ionic species. Bearing in mind the ease of polymerization of molybdenum oxyanions and the complexity of the polymers, it is not surprising that the relative proportion of these ions is found to vary with reaction conditions.

SAFETY NOTE The electrolytic cell must be housed in a fume cupboard as chlorine is evolved during the reaction.

Procedure

Reflux 10 g. molybdenum(VI) oxide with 75 ml. 12N hydrochloric acid until dissolution is almost complete. Add water slowly – keeping the solution hot – to bring the volume to 175 ml. and then transfer the mixture to the cathode compartment of the cell shown in figure 12.2.

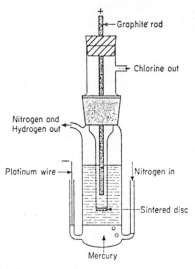

Figure 12.2. Cell for the preparation of potassium pentachloro-aquomolybdate(III).

Fill the anode chamber with 6N hydrochloric acid, to the same level as in the cathode compartment. Reduce the solution by passage of a current of about $1\frac{1}{2}$ amps at 4 volts and pass a *slow* stream of nitrogen through the electrolyte. The colour of the solution will change from light green to dark green to brown to deep red; it may take up to 24 hr. to reach the last stage, depending upon the parameters of the cell.

When there is no further colour change, transfer the air-sensitive solution, against a stream of nitrogen, to a 500 ml. flask which has been flushed well with nitrogen. Carry out all subsequent operations under nitrogen. Add a solution of 17 g. potassium chloride in 150 ml. boiled-out water and immerse the flask in an ice-bath. Pass hydrogen chloride (from a cylinder) into the solution until a red salt begins to precipitate. This is contaminated with potassium chloride and must be removed by filtration. Use an apparatus similar to that of figure 11.3. Reduce the volume of the solution by about one half by evacuation at 70°c. Cool in ice, whereupon red crystals of $K_2[MoCl_5(H_2O)]$ will form. Filter rapidly in air and wash with 12N hydrochloric acid and then with alcohol. Dry *in vacuo* and ampoule.

The above filtrate and washings contain a mixture of $K_2[MoCl_5(H_2O)]$ and $K_3[MoCl_6]$ precipitated by the alcohol. Remove by filtration and concentrate the filtrate to approximately 40 ml. at 70°c at the pump. Filter the precipitated salts and wash successively with 12N hydrochloric acid and alcohol. The alcohol causes potassium hexachloromolybdate(III), $K_3[MoCl_6]$, to precipitate in the filtrate.

Exercises

1. Investigate the reducing properties of $K_2[MoCl_5(H_2O)]$ and obtain an approximate value for its oxidation–reduction potential.
2. Determine the magnetic susceptibility of the salts and explain the results.

References

1. W. R. Bucknall, S. R. Carter and W. Wardlaw, *J. Chem. Soc.*, **1927**, 512
2. R. J. Irving and M. C. Steele, *Austral. J. Chem.*, 1957, **10**, 492.
3. K. H. Lohmann and R. C. Young, *Inorg. Synth.*, **4**, 97.

Chapter 13

Inorganic Polymers

Part of the renewed interest in inorganic chemistry in recent years has been directed towards the study of inorganic polymers, motivated in part by the search for new high-temperature-resistant materials. In a real sense much of inorganic chemistry is the chemistry of high polymers, since many compounds exist only in the solid state. Also included in most modern accounts of inorganic polymers are binuclear species such as those commonly found in cobalt and ruthenium chemistry, e.g., $[(NH_3)_3Co(OH)_3Co(NH_3)_3]Cl_3$. Of particular importance is the extensive body of knowledge on polymers containing non-metallic atoms, such as silicon, phosphorus, oxygen, boron, nitrogen and sulphur.

An important general principle in the latter types of system is the tendency for these elements to form polymer chains rather than multiple bonds. Thus, the attempt to make silicon or phosphorus analogues of carbon–carbon double bonds inevitably results in polymerization. There seem to be two main reasons for this: (a) the inadequacy of $3p$–$3p$ or $2p$–$3p$ overlap for strong π-bond formation, and (b) the strengthening of σ-bonds by π-bonds involving $3d$ orbitals. Extreme constrasts are O_2, S_8; CO_2, $(SiO_2)_n$.

Due to these tendencies, the methods of formation of inorganic polymers are generally very different from those of organic polymers. Control of the polymerization process, and therefore of the resultant physical properties, is often difficult.

This chapter contains experiments illustrating the chemistry of four important groups of polymer systems.

General References

1. F. G. R. Gimblett, *Inorganic Polymer Chemistry*, Butterworths, London, 1963.
2. *Inorganic Polymers*, Chemical Society Special Publication No. 15, London, 1961.

127

13.1 Tetrasulphur Tetranitride, S_4N_4

This compound, first prepared in 1835, is the best known of the sulphur nitrides, of which an extensive chemistry now exists. The dominant features of this chemistry are the stability of the nitrogen–sulphur bond, a tendency to anion formation, and ease of polymerization to chain or ring systems. There is very little resemblance to nitrogen–oxygen chemistry.

> SAFETY NOTE S_4N_4 *can* be violently explosive if heated above 100°c or when struck. Use a face mask and blast shield.

Procedure

$$S_2Cl_2 + Cl_2 \rightarrow 2\,SCl_2$$

$$SCl_2 + NH_3 \rightarrow S_4N_4 + S + NH_4Cl$$

Mix 200 ml. carbon tetrachloride (dried over phosphorus pentoxide) with 12·5 ml. freshly distilled disulphur dichloride, S_2Cl_2, in a 500 ml. flask (figure 13.1). Saturate the solution with chlorine (from a

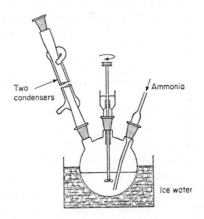

Figure 13.1. Apparatus for the preparation of tetrasulphur tetranitride.

cylinder) at room temperature, stirring rapidly, until a layer of chlorine is seen to be over the solution.

Cool the flask in ice-water and connect the inlet tube to an ammonia cylinder. Pass a fast stream of ammonia through the solution and stir as rapidly as possible, without throwing any of the reaction mixture out of the flask, keeping the temperature down to 50°C. If the stirrer will not cope with the thick mass, more carbon tetrachloride may be used. In any case, the rapid agitation of the solution will cause much of the solvent to evaporate and carbon tetrachloride should be added occasionally to keep the volume up to its initial value. It may be necessary to free the delivery tube of solid from time to time.

After some initial white fumes have formed, the colour will change from red-brown to grey-green and finally to salmon red, at which point the flow of ammonia should be stopped. The time taken to reach this point depends upon the flow of gas and the efficiency of stirring. It will probably be about 3 hr.

Filter and slurry the damp solid with 150 ml. water for about 10 min. Filter again and air-dry on a watch glass for about one day. Then shake the product with 40 ml. ether for about 20 min. (to remove sulphimide, S_7NH), filter and wash with ether once more.

Extract tetrasulphur tetranitride from the dry residue in a Soxhlet extractor, using dioxane which has been dried by (a) sodium and (b) calcium chloride. Continue until the eluate is only faintly coloured. Cool the eluate and decant from the orange-red needles of product which form. Evaporation of the mother liquor will produce another batch of crystals. Combine the batches and recrystallize from benzene. M.p. 178°C.

Exercises

1. Make a complex from your product and anhydrous nickel chloride. Reflux under nitrogen for 3 hr. 2 g. tetrasulphur tetranitride and 2·5 g. anhydrous nickel chloride in 80 ml. dry methanol. Strip off the solvent under vacuum and extract the solid residue with 50 ml. benzene. Discard this fraction (NOT down the sink!). Extract the remaining solid in the flask with three 50 ml. portions of acetone and pass down a chromatographic column of acid-washed alumina. Elute the purple band with 1:4 ethanol–acetone. A solid will be obtained on evaporation of the eluate. This may be further purified by further passes down the column. Recrystallize from acetone by slow addition of pentane.

Record the infrared spectrum of the solid and from it deduce as much as possible about the structure of the complex.

2. Relate the structures of S_4N_4, $S_4N_4H_4$, S_7NH and S_8.

References

1. M. Becke-Goehring, *Inorg. Synth.*, **6**, 123.
2. M. Becke-Goehring, *Quart. Rev.*, 1956, **10**, 437.
3. T. S. Piper, *J. Amer. Chem. Soc.*, 1958, **80**, 30.

13.2 Phosphonitrilic Halides, $(PNCl_2)_n$

The reaction of phosphorus pentachloride with ammonium chloride yields a wide range of products in varying proportions depending on the relative amounts of the reactants and the conditions employed. The general formula of the product is $(PNCl_2)_n$, $n = 3$–17. Both cyclic and linear polymers are formed by this procedure. X-ray diffraction indicates that the trimer ring has a flattened chair form in which all the P—N bonds are of equal length but shorter than the value expected for a P—N single bond. Contrary to earlier suggestions, the rings are not aromatic. Dewar has suggested that they are better regarded as being poly-allylic. The exocyclic chlorine atoms can be replaced partially or completely by various groups.

1. *Preparation of* $(PNCl_2)_n$, $n = 3, 4$

SAFETY NOTE   These compounds are toxic and should be *handled in a fume cupboard*. Some people are allergic to them.

Mix 0·30 moles phosphorus pentachloride with 0·33 moles dry finely powdered ammonium chloride and head under reflux in 120 ml. dry *sym*-tetrachloroethane. Use an oil bath at about 140°C and protect the reaction mixture with a calcium chloride guard tube. During the reaction hydrogen chloride will be evolved, and upon completion after 7–8 hr., this will cease. Cool to room temperature and filter off any unreacted ammonium chloride. Remove the solvent by vacuum distillation at a pressure of about 10 mm. mercury (or less), keeping the temperature as low as possible (40–45°C).

Extraction of the solid residue with three or four 70 ml. portions of petroleum ether (40–60°C) will leave a brown oil consisting of linear polymers. Remove the solvent from the combined extracts by vacuum evaporation, using a splash head, and transfer the remaining cyclic polymers to a *small* distilling flask. Separate the trimer and tetramer by fractional distillation using an air-cooled condenser. At 10 mm. of mercury the trimer should distil at about 140°C and will settle in the condenser. Change the condenser before distilling the tetramer which should come over near 190°C. Record the melting points.

2. *Derivatives of phosphonitrilic halides*

Part or all of the halogen in phosphonitrilic chlorides can be replaced by a variety of other groups. Prepare *one* of the following derivatives.

(a)   *2,4,6,6'-Tetra(t-butylamino)trimeric   phosphonitrilic   chloride* $P_3N_3Cl_2(NHBu^t)_4$. Add an excess of tertiary butylamine to about 1g.

(PNCl₂)₃ in 15 ml. ether. Remove the precipitated amine hydrochloride by filtration, distil off solvent and excess amine, and recrystallize the remaining solid from petroleum-ether (b.p. 60–80°C).
M.p. 155·5°C.

(b) *Trimeric phosphonitrilic isothiocyanate*, $(PN(NCS)_2)_3$. Add a
solution of 3·5 g. (PNCl₂)₃ in 20 ml. acetone to a slurry of 6 g. potassium thiocyanate in 20 ml. acetone. Take 10 min. over the addition
and agitate constantly. Heat the reaction mixture to boiling for a few
minutes, filter off the precipitated potassium chloride and wash it
with warm acetone. Cool the filtrate to −77°C for 2 hr. and filter off
the precipitated isothiocyanate derivative. Wash with cold acetone.
Recrystallize from 20 ml. n-heptane cooling to −77°C. M.p. 42°C.

NOTE   All reagents must be rigorously dry. Carry out transfer and cooling operations rapidly.

Exercises

1. Record the infrared spectra of (PNCl₂)₃ and your derivative. (i) Identify
a band characteristic of the trimer ring; (ii) assign bands due to the substituent
groups in the derivative.
2. Investigate the reaction of the linear polymer fraction with a further
quantity of ammonium chloride.
3. How are phosphonitrilic fluorides made?

References

1. L. G. Lund et al., J. Chem. Soc., **1960**, 2542.
2. S. K. Ray and R. A. Shaw, J. Chem. Soc., **1961**, 872.
3. G. Tesi et. al., J. Amer, Chem. Soc., 1960, **82**, 528.
4. N. Paddock and H. T. Searle, Adv. Inorg. Chem. Radiochem., 1959, **1**, 347.

13.3 Borazoles: $B_3H_3N_3Me_3$ and $B_3Cl_3N_3Me_3$

Borazole, $B_3N_3H_6$, is isoelectronic with benzene, which it resembles in
some of its physical and chemical properties. In contrast to benzene, it
readily adds such molecules as HCl, MeI and H₂O due to the more
localized charge distribution around the ring. Substituted borazoles
are prepared by direct routes, as in the experiments below. Borazole
and its derivatives are very susceptible to hydrolysis and the success
of any preparation depends largely on carrying out the reaction under
an inert atmosphere.

Prepare *one* of the following compounds.

1. *Preparation of N-trimethyl borazole*, $B_3H_3N_3Me_3$

Mix 5–6 g. sodium borohydride and 10 g. methyl ammonium
chloride in a 250 ml. three-neck flask under an atmosphere of dry

nitrogen. Slowly add 50 ml. triethylene glycol dimethyl ether (b.p. 222°c) from a dropping funnel, whereupon hydrogen will be evolved. Reflux until no more hydrogen is liberated. Distil the product (b.p. 134°c) and recover the solvent. Redistil the N-trimethyl borazole and transfer to tared ampoules. The triethyl analogue may be prepared similarly using 10 g. ethyl ammonium chloride and 4·8 g. sodium borohydride.

Exercises

1. Record the infrared spectrum of the compound and assign the principal bands.
2. Compare the reactions of this compound towards hydrolysis with mesitylene. Account for the differences.

Reference

D. T. Haworth and L. F. Hohnstedt, *Chem. and Ind.*, 1960, 559.

2. *Preparation of N-trimethyl B-trichloroborazole, $B_3Cl_3N_3Me_3$*

$$MeNH_2 \cdot HCl + BCl_3 \rightarrow MeNH_2 \cdot BCl_3 \xrightarrow{Et_3N} B_3Cl_3N_3Me_3 + Et_3NHCl$$

Assemble the apparatus shown in figure 13.2 and charge the flask with 9·6 g. methyl ammonium chloride and 60 ml. dry toluene. Open an ampoule of boron trichloride (Appendix 2) and transfer 15 ml. to the cold trap, which should then be cooled to −78°c. Close tap *A*, open tap *B* and pass a moderate stream of *dry* nitrogen through the apparatus for 20–30 min. Then reduce the stream to about one bubble per second and bring the contents of the flask to reflux. Open tap *A* and bring the trap up to 0°c. Then close tap *B* and allow a slow

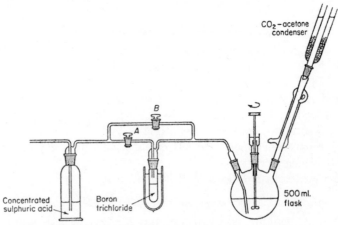

Figure 13.2. Apparatus for the preparation of N-trimethyl B-trichloroborazole.

stream of nitrogen–boron trichloride to pass into the solution. Adjust the rate of flow and the temperature of the trap so that the addition takes about 5 hr. Cool the reaction flask and remove the cold reflux head.

Add a calculated quantity of triethylamine down the condenser and stir for 10 min. Transfer the well stoppered flask to a dry-box (or -bag) and filter off the amine hydrochloride. Remove the solvent by distillation and purify the white solid residue by vacuum sublimation on the general-purpose vacuum line (120–130°c at 0·1–1 mm. mercury). If desired, recrystallize from petrol–ether–benzene. M.p. 153–156°c.

Exercises

1. Add a portion of N-trimethyl B-trichloroborazole to water at room temperature. After an hour, collect the white precipitate on a Buchner funnel and recrystallize from methanol. Record its infrared spectrum and from this try to determine the structure of the product.
2. Additional derivatives may be prepared as described in $J. Amer. Chem. Soc.$, 1960, **82**, 6248, and $J. Chem. Soc.$, **1962**, 113.

References

1. H. S. Turner and R. J. Warne, $Chem. and Ind.$, 1958, 526.
2. R. G. Jones and C. R. Kinney, $J. Amer. Chem. Soc.$, 1939, **61**, 1378.

13.4 Preparation and Polymerization of Diphenylsilanediol, Ph$_2$Si(OH)$_2$

Condensation of silanols leads to 'silicone' polymers. Commercially the most valuable are those in which alkyl groups, particularly methyl, are bound to silicon, but phenyl silicones are also useful. The silicon–phenyl bond is very stable thermally and to oxidation; these polymers therefore find use in certain high-temperature applications.

In this experiment Ph$_2$SiCl$_2$ is made and hydrolyzed in $situ$. Polymers may be formed from the solid diol by dehydration, either thermally or in the presence of catalysts.

Procedure

$$2\,PhMgCl + SiCl_4 \rightarrow Ph_2SiCl_2$$

$$Ph_2SiCl_2 + H_2O \rightarrow Ph_2Si(OH)_2 \begin{array}{l} \nearrow \;H^+ \rightarrow Ph_6Si_3O_3 \\ \searrow \;OH^- \rightarrow Ph_8Si_4O_4 \end{array}$$

A 1-litre flask is fitted with a stirrer, dropping funnel and condenser, the latter items being provided with calcium chloride guard tubes. Dry the apparatus in an oven and assemble when hot.

Place 12 g. magnesium turnings in the flask and add 50 ml. of a solution of bromobenzene (78 g.) in 250 ml. sodium dried ether. Stir and warm *very gently* until the reaction begins (the solution will turn cloudy). If necessary moderate the initial reaction by judicious cooling. Then add the remaining chlorobenzene solution at a rate which just maintains reflux conditions. Reflux for a further 15 min. with efficient stirring and then transfer to a dropping funnel.

The dropping funnel containing the Grignard reagent should now form part of an apparatus identical to that in which the Grignard reagent was prepared. Charge the flask with a solution of 17 g. silicon tetrachloride (open the ampoule as in Appendix 2) in 100 ml. dry ether. Stir well. Run in the Grignard solution over about 10 min., maintaining reflux temperature. When addition is complete, reflux for a further 2 hr.

Allow the solution to cool a little, and then hydrolyse the dichloride by *very carefully* running in dilute sulphuric acid until two layers are formed: maintain stirring. Separate the ether layer, wash twice with water and dry over anhydrous sodium sulphate. Evaporate the ether, using a large dish on a water bath. Triturate the solid residue with a little benzene and filter. Recrystallize a portion of $Ph_2Si(OH)_2$ as follows: dissolve in warm methyl ethyl ketone and add chloroform until crystals begin to separate. Redissolve these by gentle warming and allow the cooled solution to crystallize. M.p. 148°c.

Polymerization

(i) Dissolve 5 g. $Ph_2Si(OH)_2$ in 75 ml. ether and add 5 ml. concentrated hydrochloric acid. Reflux for 3 hr. Remove the ether and recrystallize from benzene and alcohol. The product is *hexaphenylcyclotrisiloxane*, $Ph_6Si_3O_3$, as white plates, m.p. 190°c.

(ii) Add two or three drops of aqueous sodium hydroxide to a boiling solution of the diol in 95% ethanol. Cool and recrystallize the precipitated *octaphenylcyclotetrasiloxane*, $Ph_8Si_4O_4$, from benzene and alcohol. The product is white needles, m.p. 201–202°c.

Exercises

1. Dehydrate a portion of diol thermally. Attempt to identify the product.
2. Discuss the structures and uses of methyl silicone polymers.

References

1. S. D. Rosenberg, J. J. Walburn and H. E. Ramsden, *J. Org. Chem.*, 1957, **22**, 1606.
2. C. H. Burkhard, *J. Amer. Chem. Soc.*, 1945, **67**, 2173.

Chapter 14

High-Pressure Techniques

SAFETY NOTE   The experiments in this chapter should only be attempted by students of above average manipulative skill. Close supervision is essential and work in pairs is advised.

Do not include these preparations in a course unless adequate fume cupboard and other facilities are available.

Extensive use is made of high-pressure techniques in synthetic inorganic chemistry, one of the most important general fields of application being in the chemistry of metal carbonyls and their complexes. Most research groups nowadays are equipped with autoclaves which may be safely used up to 350 atmospheres. Equipment for use up to 3000 atmospheres is in regular use in a few laboratories. Reactions which proceed at moderate pressures, and for which a small-scale preparation is acceptable, may be carried out in a small 'bomb' rather than an autoclave. The reactions given below require the use of a steel 'bomb' which may be used safely to 140 atmospheres (see figure 14.1).

14.1 Preparation of Iron Carbonyl Iodide, $FeI_2(CO)_4$

The stability of the carbonyl halides, $FeX_2(CO)_4$, increases from X = chloride to bromide to iodide. The preparation of the iodide is particularly simple as the reaction proceeds in the cold.

$$FeI_2 + 4 CO \rightarrow FeI_2(CO)_4$$

(i) Prepare anhydrous ferrous iodide by reacting stoicheiometric amounts of iodine and iron powder (suspended in dry methanol). Filter, evaporate excess solvent and dry $in\ vacuo$ with slight heating.

The black product is ferrous iodide. Moisture will cause colour changes to green or yellow.

(ii) Transfer approximately $\frac{1}{2}$ g. ferrous iodide to a 25 ml. 'bomb', assemble and connect to a cylinder of carbon monoxide. Pressurize to 100–120 atmospheres, close the cylinder and 'bomb' valves and disconnect. Allow to stand for 10 hr. or longer. Open the 'bomb' valve slowly – in a fume cupboard – and allow excess gas to escape.

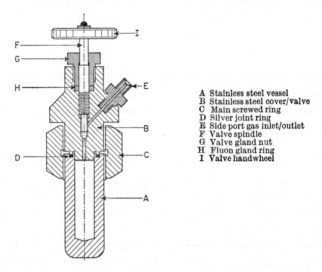

A Stainless steel vessel
B Stainless steel cover/valve
C Main screwed ring
D Silver joint ring
E Side port gas inlet/outlet
F Valve spindle
G Valve gland nut
H Fluon gland ring
I Valve handwheel

Figure 14.1. Reaction 'bomb'. (By courtesy of Baskerville and Lindsay, Ltd.)

Exercises

Record the infrared spectra of the product in (a) cyclohexane, (b) chloroform, in the 2200–1600 cm.$^{-1}$ region. Is the compound *cis* or *trans*? How do you explain the change in the observed frequencies from cyclohexane to chloroform?

References

1. W. Hieber and H. Lagally, *Z. anorg. Chem.*, 1940, **245**, 295.
2. C. G. Barraclough, J. Lewis, and R. S. Nyholm, *J. Chem. Soc.*, **1961**, 2582.

14.2 Preparation of Perfluorotetramethyleneirontetracarbonyl, $[\mathrm{Fe(CO)_4(CF_2)_4}]$

Transition metals often form fluorocarbon complexes which are of great stability and of structural types not formed from hydrocarbons. This experiment deals with a typical example from iron chemistry.

Preliminary reading: *general vacuum-line technique* (*Chapter* 8)

(i) Prepare tetrafluororoethylene, C_2F_4, by cracking about 5 g. polytetrafluoroethylene ('Teflon') powder contained in a silica bottle under vacuum at 500°C. Condense the gas in a trap cooled in liquid nitrogen.

(ii) Transfer about 3 g. iron tetracarbonyl, $Fe_3(CO)_{12}$, to a 25 ml. 'bomb', assemble and evacuate on the general-purpose vacuum line. Cool with liquid nitrogen and allow the tetrafluoroethylene to condense onto the carbonyl. Close the 'bomb', allow it to warm to room temperature and transfer to an oven at 110°C in a fume cupboard. Leave for 24 hr.

(iii) Reconnect the 'bomb' to the vacuum line and pump off volatile products into a cold trap, which should be allowed to warm up in a fume cupboard when the experiment is finished. The solid remaining in the 'bomb' should now be transferred to a sublimation apparatus and sublimed at 40°C under vacuum onto a cold-finger at −78°C.

Exercises

1. Record the infrared spectrum and identify the carbonyl and C—F stretching frequencies. Compare the carbonyl frequencies with those of other disubstituted irontetracarbonyl derivatives and try to explain any differences.
2. What is the structure of the complex? Compare it with the products obtained from reaction of irontetracarbonyl with octafluorocyclohexa-1,3- or -1,4-diene.

References

1. H. H. Hoehn *et. al.*, *J. Chem. Soc.*, **1961**, 2738.
2. R. S. Nyholm, *Proc. Chem. Soc.*, 1961, 282.
3. M. R. Churchill and R. Mason, *Ibid*, **1963**, 365.

14.3 Preparation of Anhydrous Metal Chlorides

Anhydrous metal chlorides can sometimes be prepared from the corresponding oxides or sulphides by reaction with carbon tetrachloride under pressure. This can be advantageous if the oxide or sulphide is cheap and/or readily available. The method is of wide applicability. The following preparation is only one of many examples which might be chosen. Discuss your choice of preparation with the demonstrator.

Preparation of tungsten hexachloride, WCl_6

$$WO_3 + 3 \, CCl_4 \rightarrow WCl_6 + 3 \, COCl_2$$

The reaction tube for this experiment is an ampoule of approximately 50 ml. volume made of standard wall Pyrex. Load it with 2 g. commercial tungsten(VI) oxide and 8 ml. carbon tetrachloride for every 26 ml. of the tube (i.e., about 16 ml.). Cool the ampoule and seal, annealing the top thoroughly (Appendix 2). Place the ampoule in a 100 ml. 'bomb' and support it loosely with glass wool. Pour in 8 ml. carbon tetrachloride for each 26 ml. free space left in the 'bomb'. Close the 'bomb' and transfer to the bomb oven. Heat to 400°c and maintain this temperature for 3 hr. When cool, open the bomb carefully. Release pressure in the ampoule *in an efficient fume cupboard* by opening a small vent hole with a fine-jet flame – point the ampoule away from yourself. Then crack off the neck and stopper it. Transfer to a dry-bag. Remove about half of the solvent by evaporation, filter and wash with carbon tetrachloride. Purify by vacuum sublimation. Seal into tared ampoules.

Exercises

1. Determine tungsten in a sample of your product.
2. List the other known metal halides of the type MCl_6.
3. Metals frequently exhibit their highest oxidation states in oxides and fluorides. Discuss and explain.

References

1. K. Knox *et. al., J. Amer. Chem. Soc.,* 1957, **79**, 3358.
2. A. B. Bardawil, F. N. Collier, and S. Y. Tyree, *Inorg. Chem.,* 1964, **3**, 149.
3. L. E. Orgel, *Introduction to Transition Metal Chemistry,* Methuen, London, 1960.

Chapter 15

Ultraviolet and Visible Spectroscopy

Electronic transitions in molecules and ions correspond, energetically, to quanta of light in the ultraviolet–visible region of the spectrum (see inside front cover). In particular, transitions between energy levels in transition-metal ions occur mainly in the range 7500–40,000 cm.$^{-1}$, for which instrumentation is both well developed and plentiful. Evidence from ultraviolet–visible spectra has been immensely important in the formulation and testing of theories of transition-metal chemistry. Other uses of ultraviolet–visible spectroscopy in inorganic chemistry include studies of kinetics and of complex formation in solution (see experiment below).

Instrumentation

Two types of light source are in common use: the tungsten filament lamp for the visible and near-infrared region and the hydrogen lamp for wavelengths shorter than about 330 mμ. Dispersion is by a prism of glass or quartz and detection is effected by a photomultiplier or by a lead sulphide photoconductive cell at the red end. Detail and operation of the instruments vary widely according to whether they are manual, automatic or semi-automatic.

Units and conversion factors

Wavelengths of radiation in the ultraviolet–visible region are generally quoted in millimicrons, mμ:

$$1 \text{ m}\mu = 10-\text{e } \mu = 10 \text{ Å}$$

When studying transition-metal-ion spectra one is generally interested in the energy difference between the quantum levels involved in the observed transition. Absorption maxima are therefore quoted in terms of reciprocal centimetres, cm.$^{-1}$, a unit which is directly proportional to energy.

$$Energy = h \times frequency$$

$$= h \times wavelength$$

where h = Planck's constant and c = the velocity of light

Other useful units are related as follows:

$$1 \text{ ev} = 8066 \text{ cm.}^{-1} = 23 \cdot 05 \text{ kcal./mole}$$

$$1 \text{ kcal./mole} = 349 \cdot 9 \text{ cm.}^{-1}$$

Sample cells and their care

Cells are of quartz (for ultraviolet work) or glass and are supplied and used in matched pairs. For gases, cells of up to 10 cm. path length are used; for highly absorbent liquids path lengths down to 0·025 mm. may be necessary. Long-path cells are used when weakly absorbing, or very dilute, samples are under examination. For any given system the best cell thickness can be deduced from the Beer–Lambert Law. For most purposes 1 cm. cells are suitable.

Cells must be carefully washed and dried after use; matching pairs must be kept together. They should always be handled by the sides (the ground faces) and any spills must be wiped off carefully with tissue. Stoppers or lids should be used to eliminate evaporation of solvent.

15.1 Rate of Isomerism of *Cis*-Dichlorobis(ethylenediamine) cobalt(III) chloride, [Co(en)₂Cl₂]Cl

Prepare approximately 2×10^{-3} M solutions of the compounds *cis*- and *trans*-[Co(en)₂Cl₂]Cl (use stock samples or prepare as below); dissolve *equal* amounts in 10 ml. methanol. Record the spectrum of each isomer over the range 350–700 mμ. Notice that the band maximum of the *cis*-isomer at 540 mμ coincides with a minimum in the spectrum of the *trans*-isomer. Thus, by following the change of optical density with time of a *cis-trans* solution of [Co(en)₂Cl₂]Cl at 540 mμ, their rate of interconversion may be determined.

Theory

The process is first-order; the rate equation is therefore

$$\log_e[cis] = -kt + c \tag{1}$$

Since the concentration of the *cis*-form at any time, t, is proportional to the difference between the optical densities of the *cis*-form and of the partially isomerized solution, equation (1) can be written

$$\log_e[D_t - D_\infty] = -kt + c \qquad (2)$$

where $D_t =$ the optical density after time t, and $D_\infty =$ the optical density at infinite time, i.e., when isomerization is complete.

Measurement of rate of isomerism

Prepare 100 ml. approximately 2×10^{-3} M solution of *cis*-[Co(en)$_2$Cl$_2$]Cl in methanol and thermostat at 40°C in a water-bath. Withdraw samples every 10 min., cool rapidly to stop further isomerization and determine the optical density of the sample at 540 mμ. Leave one sample in the thermostat overnight before determining its optical density: this is effectively the D_∞ value.

Plot $\log_e[D_t - D_\infty]$ versus t and determine the half-life of the conversion.

Exercises

1. Why does the *cis*-isomer absorb light, in the range studied, about four times as strongly as the *trans*-isomer?
2. By what mechanism does the isomerization process take place?

References

1. L. K. Brice, *J. Chem. Educ.*, 1962, **39**, 634.
2. D. D. Brown and C. K. Ingold, *J. Chem. Soc.*, **1953**, 2680.

Preparation of cis- and trans-[Co(en)$_2$Cl$_2$]Cl

$$CoCl_2 + en + HCl \xrightarrow{[O]} trans\text{-}[Co(en)_2Cl_2]Cl \cdot HCl + H_2O$$

(a) To 16 g. cobaltous chloride, CoCl$_2 \cdot$ 6 H$_2$O, in 50 ml. water, add 60 ml. of a 10% solution of ethylenediamine. Add 10 ml. concentrated hydrochloric acid and draw air through the solution for 10–12 hr. (not longer, otherwise side reactions may occur). Add 35 ml. concentrated hydrochloric acid to the resulting purple solution and evaporate on a steam bath until a crust forms on the surface. Allow the solution to stand overnight and then filter off the green square crystals of the hydrochloride. Recrystallize the product by dissolving it in the minimum of warm 1 : 5 concentrated hydrochloric acid–water; wash the green crystals with ethanol and then with ether. Heat the crystals to 110°C for 2 hr. to remove hydrogen chloride.

(b) Dissolve half of the above product in water and evaporate the

solution to dryness on a steam bath. Repeat this procedure *once* more
and then remove unchanged *trans*-isomer by washing with a little
ice-cold water.

Reference

J. C. Bailar, *Inorg. Synth.*, **2**, 222.

15.2 The Influence of Ligand-Field Strength upon the Spectra of Cu(II) Complexes

The visible spectrum of an aqueous solution containing Cu^{2+} ions
consists of a single unsymmetrical broad band. This is due to the
electronic transition $(t_{2_g})^6(e_g)^3 \rightarrow (t_{2_g})^5(e_g)^4$ in the octahedral complex
ion $[Cu(H_2O)_6]^{2+}$. As ammonia is added to this solution, water
molecules are replaced by ammonia and the whole family of complex
ions, $[Cu(H_2O)_n(NH_3)_{6-n}]^{2+}$ ($n = 1$ to 6), can be prepared in solution.
Since ammonia creates a stronger ligand field than water, successive
substitution of ammonia for water results in a shift of λ_{max} to shorter
wavelengths.

Procedure

The following solutions are necessary for the experiment:

   (a) 100 ml. exactly M $Cu(NO_3)_2 \cdot 3 H_2O$ in water,

   (b) 100 ml. 2 M ammonium nitrate,

   (c) standardized solutions of ammonium hydroxide, exactly M,
2 M and 3 M respectively.

Using these solutions, prepare aqueous solutions of the ions
$[Cu(H_2O)_n(NH_3)_{6-n}]^{2+}$ ($n = 1$ to 6), as follows.

   (i) To 5 ml. copper solution (a), add solid ammonium nitrate until
saturated. Then add slowly 5 ml. M ammonium hydroxide. Add
further solid ammonium nitrate to re-saturate. Dilute 1 ml. of this
solution to 25 ml. with 2M ammonium nitrate. The resulting solution
contains $[Cu(H_2O)_5(NH_3)]^{2+}$.

   (ii) Repeat (i) twice but use 2 M and 3 M ammonium hydroxide
instead of the M solution and thereby prepare solutions of
$[Cu(H_2O)_4(NH_3)_2]^{2+}$ and $[Cu(H_2O)_3(NH_3)_3]^{2+}$ respectively.

   (iii) Add 1 ml. 0·880 ammonia solution to 1 ml. copper solution (a).
Dilute this solution to 50 ml. with water, giving $[Cu(H_2O)_2(NH_3)_4]^{2+}$.

   (iv) Dilute $\frac{1}{2}$ ml. copper solution (a) to 25 ml. with 0·880 ammonia
to give $[Cu(H_2O)(NH_3)_5]^{2+}$ in solution.

   (v) Dilute $\frac{1}{2}$ ml. copper solution (a) to 25 ml. with water.

NOTE 1. Ammonium nitrate is used to prevent hydrolysis of the complexes with $n = 3, 4$ and 5.

2. The above solutions (i) to (v) give suitable absorbancies in 1 cm. cells on the Unicam SP500 and SP600 spectrophotometers.

Record the spectra of the above solutions over the range 500 to 1000 mμ.

Exercises

1. Correlate the positions of $\lambda_{max.}$ with the number of molecules of ammonia in the complex. Comment upon the position of $\lambda_{max.}$ for $[Cu(H_2O)(NH_3)_5]^{2+}$.
2. Comment upon the shapes of the observed bands.
3. How would you prepare $[Cu(NH_3)_6]^{2+}$? Where would you expect its $\lambda_{max.}$ to lie?

Reference

J. Bjerrum, C. J. Ballhausen and C. K. Jorgensen, *Acta. Chem. Scand.*, 1954, **8**, 1275.

15.3 Spectrophotometric Determination of the Composition of a Complex Ion using Job's Method

The ultraviolet–visible spectra of a series of complexes of the form ML$_n$ will vary with the number of ligands, L. Each complex can be characterized by the wavelength at which the absorption is a maximum. If, to a solution of a metal ion, M, varying amounts of ligand solution are added, various complexes will be formed depending on the relative proportions of M and L.

$$M + n\,L \rightleftharpoons ML_n \tag{1}$$

The complexes ML$_n$ formed in solution can be identified as described below by a procedure due to Job (1928), known as the method of continuous variations.

Procedure

Study one of the following systems.

(i) *Chromate–H$_3$O$^+$ system.* Solutions required:

0·1 M potassium chromate
0·1 M hydrochloric acid

Using these, prepare acid–chromate mixtures in which the mole fraction of acid, x, is 0·2, 0·3, 0·4, 0·5, 0·6, 0·7 and 0·8, and the overall molarity is 0·01 M. A 0·01 M solution of potassium chromate is also needed.

Measure the optical density of each of these solutions at 15 mμ intervals between 470 and 560 mμ.

(ii) *Ni^{2+}–ethylenediamine system.* Solutions required:

> 0·1 M nickel sulphate
> 0·1 M ethylenediamine hydrochloride

Using these, prepare mixtures in which the mole fraction of ethylenediamine, x, is 0·3, 0·4, 0·5, 0·6, 0·7, 0·8 and 0·9. Measure the optical density of each of these solutions, together with that of the 0·1 M nickel sulphate, at 530, 545, 578, 622 and 640 mμ.

Theory

$$\text{Optical density, } D = \log(I_0/I_t)$$

where $I_0 =$ the intensity of the incident light and $I_t =$ the intensity of the transmitted light.

By the Beer–Lambert law,

$$\log(I_0/I_t) = \varepsilon C t,$$

where $\varepsilon =$ the molar extinction coefficient, $C =$ the molar concentration, and $t =$ the thickness of the solution.

$$\therefore D = \varepsilon C t$$

Since the optical density of a solution is the sum of the optical densities of the contained species,

$$D_{\text{measured}} = (\varepsilon_M C_M + \varepsilon_L C_L + \varepsilon_{ML_n} C_{ML_n})t$$

If there had been no interaction, the optical density would have been

$$D_{\text{theoretical}} = (\varepsilon_M M(1 - x) + \varepsilon_L M x)t$$

where M is the molar concentration of M and L. If Y is the difference between D_{measured} and $D_{\text{theoretical}}$,

$$Y = [\varepsilon_M C_M + \varepsilon_L C_L + \varepsilon_{ML_n} C_{ML_n} - (\varepsilon_M M(1 - x) + \varepsilon_L M x)t]$$

Plot a graph of Y against n for each wavelength. For a 1 cm. cell Y now simplifies to

$$Y = D_{\text{measured}} - (1 - x)D_M$$

(ε_L is zero since the ligand has no absorption at the wavelengths concerned and D_M is the optical density of the pure CrO_4^{2-} or Ni^{2+} solution.)

The maxima in these curves occur at mole fractions, x, where complex formation takes place. Deduce the formulae of the complexes present in solution.

Exercise

What other properties could be used to investigate this type of system by the method of continuous variations?

Reference

1. W. C. Vosburgh and G. R. Cooper, *J. Amer. Chem. Soc.*, 1941, **63**, 437.
2. O. E. Lanford and J. R. Quinan, *J. Amer. Chem. Soc.*, 1948, **70**, 2900.

Chapter 16

Magnetochemistry

Magnetochemistry is of particular importance in the study of transition-metal compounds, due to the special properties of partially filled d-shells, although other important applications exist. Unique information about the arrangement of d-electrons can be obtained from a single measurement of susceptibility, whilst further information will often come from a knowledge of its temperature dependence. We give here the minimum of theory necessary to understand the experiments. Before attempting to interpret your results, read the recommended general references.

Theory

If a substance is placed in a magnetic field of intensity H, then the intensity of the field within the substance may be either less than or greater than H. In the first case the substance is said to be 'diamagnetic', in the second, 'paramagnetic'. In other words, diamagnetic bodies are less permeable and paramagnetic bodies more permeable than a vacuum to magnetic lines of force. Diamagnetism is a universal property of matter; it is a volume effect and is smaller in magnitude than paramagnetism, which is a property of substances possessing unpaired electrons.

In a field of intensity H, the intensity within a substance, B, is given by

$$B = H + 4\pi I \qquad (1)$$

I is the intensity of magnetization. The quantity $I/H = \kappa$ is called the volume susceptibility of the substance. It is this quantity which is determined by almost all experimental methods. The susceptibility per unit mass is known as χ and is simply κ/d, where d is the density of the substance. The molar susceptibility, χ_M, is the magnetic susceptibility per gram-molecular weight.

The magnetic moment, μ, in Bohr magnetons is given by the formula

$$\mu = \sqrt{\left(\frac{3k\chi'_M T}{N\beta^2}\right)} \qquad (2)$$

where $k =$ Boltzmann's constant, $T =$ absolute temperature, $N =$ Avogadro's number, $\beta =$ the Bohr magneton and $\chi'_M =$ the susceptibility corrected for diamagnetism.

This reduces to

$$\mu = 2\cdot83\sqrt{(\chi'_M T)} \qquad (3)$$

In a complex, the molar susceptibility measured is the sum of those due to the paramagnetic metal ion and the diamagnetic ligands and

Table 16.1 Diamagnetic corrections. (All values $\times 10^{-6}$/g. ion or molecule.)

Ca^{2+}	9	BF_4^-	39	acetate	32
Co^{2+}	12	Br^-	35	acetylacetonate	55
Co^{3+}	10	BrO_3^-	40	oxalate	34
Cr^{2+}	15	CN^-	16	ethylenediamine	46
Cr^{3+}	11	CNO^-	21	triphenylphosphine	167
Cs^+	33	CNS^-	33	NH_3	18
Cu^{2+}	11	CO_3^-	32	H_2O	13
Fe^{2+}	13	Cl^-	25		
Fe^{3+}	10	ClO_3^-	31		
Hg^{2+}	38	ClO_4^-	33		
K^+	14	F^-	10		
Li^+	1	I^-	51		
Mg^{2+}	4	IO_3^-	51		
Mn^{2+}	14	IO_4^-	53		
Mn^{3+}	10	NO_2^-	10		
Mo^{4+}	17	NO_3^-	19		
NH_4^+	12	O^{2-}	12		
$(NMe_4)^+$	52	OH^-	12		
$(NEt_4)^+$	101	SO_3^{2-}	38		
Na^+	6	SO_4^{2-}	40		
Ni^{2+}	12	$S_2O_3^{2-}$	49		
Rb^+	21	$S_2O_8^{2-}$	78		
Zn^{2+}	15				

For other ligands or ions see:

1. J. Lewis and R. G. Wilkins, *Modern Coordination Chemistry*, Interscience, London, 1960, p. 403.
2. P. W. Selwood, *Magnetochemistry*, Interscience, London, 1956, chapters 5 and 6.
3. G. Foëx, C. J. Gorter and L. J. Smits, *Constantes Sélectionées Diamagnetisme et Paramagnetisme*, Masson, Paris, 1957.

ions. Hence a correction has to be made in order to determine the susceptibility of the metal ion alone:

$$\chi_M(\text{complex}) = \chi'_M(\text{metal ion}) + \chi_M(\text{ligands}) + \chi_M(\text{ions}) \qquad (4)$$

Table 16.1 gives the molar susceptibility of a number of the more common ligands and ions. Thus, from a determination of χ_M at temperature, T, the magnetic moment of a substance (in Bohr magnetons) may be calculated.

Experimental

There are two commonly used methods of measuring magnetic susceptibilities: the Faraday method and the Gouy method. In the Faraday method, the force on a very small specimen is measured directly, whereas in the Gouy method, the force integrated over a large field gradient is measured. The former method has advantages if only very small samples (~ 1 mg.) are available and is very useful in measurements of magnetic anisotropy in single crystals. Unfortunately, there are practical difficulties in the construction and use of the equipment because of the small forces measured. The specimen in the Gouy method consists of a long rod of solid or solution in a tube. One end is in a region of uniform field and the other in a zero or very small field. Since much larger forces are involved they are conveniently measured with a conventional balance. This is the most frequently used method.

Equipment for measuring magnetic moments at room temperature using the Gouy method

The magnet A permanent magnet or electromagnet with a field of between 5000 and 10,000 gauss is necessary. In order that the field be homogeneous, the pole faces should be as large as possible and the pole gap as small as possible. In practice the minimum dimensions for both the pole faces and pole gap are about ½ in. The magnet should be mounted on a screw-drive device so that it can be positioned accurately and also, in the case of a permanent magnet, be removed from the vicinity of the suspended specimen.

The balance should weigh to 0·01 mg. and cause minimal vertical movement of the specimen. This usually necessitates a balance with rider adjustments and becomes essential when a magnet with small pole faces is used.

The specimen Internally flat-bottom glass or Perspex tubes are used for holding the sample, which may be either a homogeneous powder or a concentrated solution. The tube should have a scratch mark 2–3 in. above the bottom and always be filled to this mark. Filling the tube with solid requires care – the powdered or fine crystalline material should be introduced a little at a time. After each addition gently tap the tube on a hard surface before adding more powder.

Figure 16.1 shows the arrangement of the specimen suspended from the left-hand balance pan and surrounded by a glass tube to shield it from draughts. The tube contains a pocket for a thermometer.

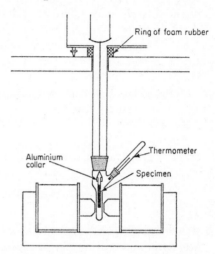

Figure 16.1. Single-temperature Gouy Balance. (By courtesy of Newport Instruments, Ltd.)

Sometimes the specimen may swing towards one of the pole faces and incorrect measurements will result. This usually occurs when the compound under consideration has a high susceptibility. The trouble can be eliminated either by reducing the strength of the magnetic field or by diluting the sample.

Procedure For *solid samples* carry out the following weighings, 1–5. The steps in the calculation are indicated.

1. Weight of tube empty, out of field = g.
2. Weight of tube filled to the mark with distilled water = g.
   Volume of tube, $v = (2 - 1) \div d$ = ml.
3. Weight of tube empty, in field = g.
   Repulsion due to tube, $\Delta r = (1 - 3)$ = g.
4. Weight of tube filled to the mark with solid, out of field = g.
5. Weight of tube filled to the mark with solid, in field = g.
   Attraction due to tube and solid, $\Delta t = (5 - 4)$ = g.
   Attraction due to solid only, $\Delta w = \Delta t + \Delta r$ = g.
   Weight of solid, $m = (4 - 1)$ = g.

Substitute in the equation

$$\chi \cdot_m - \kappa_a \cdot v = B \cdot \Delta w$$

where χ = susceptibility of substance/g., κ_a = volume susceptibility of air = $0 \cdot 029 \times 10^{-6}$, B = the calibration constant of the tube (dependent upon field strength), and d = density of distilled water.

Repeat to obtain results consistent to 1%.

If the *sample is a solution*, the scheme outlined above must be slightly modified. Weigh the tube filled to the mark with solvent in and out of the field to obtain Δr, and then weigh the tube filled with solution in and out of the field to obtain Δt.

Calibration   Determine the constant, B, in the formula above using one of the following compounds for which the molar susceptibility is accurately known.

Solid standards

1. Mercury tetrathiocyanatocobalt(II), Hg[Co(NCS)$_4$]

For the preparation see experiment 5.6.

$$\chi = 16 \cdot 44 \times 10^{-6} \text{ at } 20°\text{c}; \quad \frac{d\chi}{dT} = -0 \cdot 05 \times 10^{-6}$$

2. Tris(ethylenediamine)nickel(II) thiosulphate, [Ni(en)$_3$]S$_2$O$_3$

Add a boiling solution of 8 g. sodium thiosulphate pentahydrate in 80 ml. water to a boiling solution of 8 g. nickel nitrate, Ni(NO$_3$)$_2 \cdot$ 6 H$_2$O, and 8 ml. ethylenediamine hydrate in 20 ml. water. Boil for 1 min. and stir vigorously whilst the mixture cools. Filter, wash with cold water, then ethanol and dry at 100°c.

$$\chi = 11 \cdot 04 \times 10^{-6} \text{ at } 20°\text{c}; \quad \frac{d\chi}{dT} = -0 \cdot 04 \times 10^{-6}$$

Reference

N. F. Curtis, *J. Chem. Soc.*, **1961**, 3147.

Solution standards

Ferrous ammonium sulphate, (NH$_4$)$_2$Fe(SO$_4$)$_2 \cdot$ 6 H$_2$O

$$\chi = 32 \cdot 3 \times 10^{-6} \text{ at } 20°\text{c}$$

NOTE   A freshly prepared sample should be used.

Once a particular tube has been calibrated, and provided the magnetic field is kept constant, the calibration need not be repeated.

General references

1. J. Lewis and R. G. Wilkins, *Modern Coordination Chemistry*, Interscience, London, 1960, chapter 6.
2. P. W. Selwood, *Magnetochemistry*, Interscience, London, 1956.

16.1 Magnetochemistry of Some Nickel(II) Complexes

Nickel(II) complexes may be octahedral, square planar or tetrahedral in configuration. In general these stereochemistries may be distinguished from one another by the evidence—taken together—of their colours, molar absorbances and magnetic susceptibilities. The latter show some interesting features which nicely illustrate several important points in magnetochemical theory. In fact, the values of their magnetic moments serve as a useful diagnostic tool for the differentiation of four and six coordinate nickel(II) compounds.

Procedure

Do *either* Experiment A *or* Experiment B.
A.
Determine the magnetic moments of the following solids.

   (i) [Ni(NH₃)₆](BF₄)₂
   (ii) KNiF₃
   (iii) K(Ni₀.₂Zn₀.₈)F₃

B.
Determine the magnetic moments of the following solids.

   (i) [NEt₄]₂[NiCl₄]
   (ii) [NiCl₂(PPh₃)₂]
   (iii) K₂[Ni(CN)₄]

Where available use stock samples; otherwise prepare as detailed below.

Calculate the magnetic moments that you would expect for your compounds on the basis of the 'spin only' formula. Explain any deviations of your experimental values from this figure.

Preparations

Hexa-amminenickel(II) fluorborate, [Ni(NH₃)₆](BF₄)₂. Dissolve 6 g. hydrated nickel chloride in 10 ml. warm water and add 12 ml. concentrated (0·880) ammonia solution. Stir until all the precipitated nickel hydroxide has dissolved and the liquid contains crystals of hexa-amminenickel chloride. Add water slowly until the crystals *just* redissolve and remove any residue by filtration. Dissolve 5 g. ammonium fluorbate in the minimum of dilute ammonia solution and add to the hexa-amminenickel solution. Stir and filter off the crystals of hexa-amminenickel fluorborate; wash with dilute ammonia solution until the filtrate is colourless and then with acetone. Dry in air. A suspension of the crystals in water is almost invisible because their refractive index is approximately that of water.

Potassium trifluoronickelate, $KNiF_3$. See experiment 5.7.

$K(Ni_{0.2}Zn_{0.8})F_3$. Prepare as for $KNiF_3$, using appropriate portions of nickel and zinc salts.

Tetraethylammonium tetrachloronickelate, $[NEt_4]_2[NiCl_4]$. See Experiment 9.2.

Dichlorobis (triphenylphosphine) nickel(II), $[NiCl_2(PPh_3)_2]$. Dissolve stoicheiometric quantities of hydrated nickel chloride and triphenylphosphine in *either* n-butanol *or* glacial acetic acid, and stand overnight. Filter the product, wash with solvent and dry *in vacuo*.

Potassium tetracyanonickelate, $K_2[Ni(CN)_4]$. Dissolve 12 g. hydrated nickel sulphate in 40 ml. water. Slowly add to this solution 6 g. potassium cyanide in 14 ml. water. Filter the precipitated nickel cyanide and wash it well to remove occluded potassium sulphate. Add this solid nickel cyanide to 6 g. potassium cyanide in 6 ml. water. Warm the red solution formed until small crystals form, redissolve them and allow to cool. Remove the crystals by filtration and evaporate the filtrate to obtain a further crop of crystals. Remove water of hydration by drying at 100°C.

References

1. J. Lewis and R. G. Wilkins, *Modern Coordination Chemistry*, Interscience, London, 1960, Chapter 6.
2. D. J. Machin, R. L. Martin and R. S. Nyholm, *J. Chem. Soc.*, **1963**, 1490.
3. Palmer, *Experimental Inorganic Chemistry*, pp. 554; 557; 558.

16.2 Magnetochemistry of Some Iron Complexes

The majority of iron complexes are octahedral, although some tetrahedral species are known for both Fe(II) and Fe(III). Given also the possibility of high-spin or low-spin configuration in the octahedral case, depending upon the strength of the ligand field, it is clear that the magnetochemistry of iron complexes can be interesting. This experiment illustrates some different types of behaviour.

Procedure

Determine the magnetic moments of the following compounds as solids:

(i) $K_3[Fe(C_2O_4)_3] \cdot 3 H_2O$

(ii) $K_3[Fe(CN)_6]$

(iii) $[NEt_4]_2[Fe^{(II)}Cl_4]$

(iv) $[NEt_4][Fe^{(III)}Cl_4]$

Use stock samples of (i) and (ii). Prepare (iii) and (iv) as below.

Compare your experimental magnetic moments with those calculated on the basis of the 'spin-only' formula. Discuss mechanisms whereby deviations from the 'spin-only' values may be explained.

Bis(tetraethylammonium)tetrachloroiron(II). Mix, under nitrogen, fairly concentrated solutions of calculated amounts of ferrous chloride and tetraethylammonium chloride in boiled-out ethanol. The pale-green crystalline product forms immediately. Filter rapidly and do not recrystallize: decomposition occurs in hot alcohol.

Tetraethylammoniumtetrachloroiron(III). Reflux a calculated quantity of ferric chloride (or ferrous chloride) with a slight excess (1 g.) of tetraethylammonium chloride in 20 ml. freshly distilled thionyl chloride until dissolution is complete. Concentrate to half volume at the pump using a splash-head. Refrigerate until the pale-green product crystallizes. Wash the crystals with small portions of cold thionyl chloride and dry *in vacuo*.

Exercise

How many lines would you expect to find in the ultraviolet–visible spectra of compounds (i) and (ii) above?

References

1. J. Lewis and R. G. Wilkins, *Modern Coordination Chemistry*, Interscience, London, 1960.
2. N. S. Gill, *J. Chem. Soc.*, **1961**, 3512.
3. D. M. Adams *et. al.*, *J. Chem. Soc.*, **1963**, 2189.

Chapter 17

X-Ray Powder Photography

The positions and intensities of the lines which make up an X-ray diffraction photograph are determined by the spacing of the layers of ions or molecules within the crystal, and the arrangement within these layers. This makes the diffraction pattern of any given substance highly characteristic (though not necessarily unique), and provides a means of identification. The technique of X-ray powder photography is convenient to apply since it requires only powder specimens and very small quantities of sample (say, 100 μg.). It is non-destructive, and the sample may be contained within a glass or quartz tube for protection from the atmosphere.

Applications to inorganic chemistry are many and various. For example, a crystalline reaction product might be identified rapidly and a decision made as to which of two or more possible phase modifications it has adopted. Information is often obtained by this technique which would be otherwise inaccessible. Identification is by comparison with the pattern of an authentic sample or by searching a collection of diffraction data until a match is made. The American Society for Testing Materials (A.S.T.M.) have published a collection of data on powder patterns for over 5000 compounds. For comparison purposes, it is usual to list d values (i.e., the distances between crystal planes responsible for the observed diffraction lines) as these are independent of the geometry of the camera and of the wavelength of the X-rays used.

If the material under examination has high crystal symmetry, it may also be possible to make some observations about the positions of atoms within the unit cell. Indexing, and so finding the symmetry of the unit cell of a material whose symmetry is less than cubic, is tedious, and becomes prohibitively so if the symmetry is less than orthorhombic (i.e., three unknown parameters). Other applications include proof of isomorphism, the determination of phase-transition temperatures and the investigation of non-stoicheiometry.

Theory

A crystal with planes oriented at an angle θ to an incident X-ray beam of wavelength λ will diffract the rays according to the equation

$$\lambda = 2d \sin \theta \tag{1}$$

where d is the interplanar spacing. In a powder the crystallites are randomly oriented: a specimen illuminated with a narrow pencil of monochromatic X-rays will therefore give rise to a series of diffraction cones of half angle 2θ (see figure 17.1). The intersection of a curved

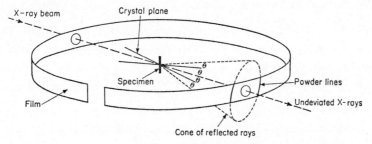

Figure 17.1. Arrangement of film in a Straumanis camera, showing one diffraction cone.

strip of film with these diffraction cones gives the familiar powder photograph, which consists of a series of curved lines. There are three commonly used ways of mounting film in cameras for powder work. We describe here that due to Straumanis, as the worked example below refers to a film taken by this method. As can be seen from figure 17.1, the film is mounted asymmetrically around the circumference of the camera, entrance and exit holes being provided for the beam. Reflections corresponding to high θ-values are centred about the entry hole and those of low θ-values around the exit hole.

For crystals of the cubic system, the unit cell dimension, a, is related to d by the expression

$$d = a/\sqrt{(h^2 + k^2 + l^2)} \tag{2}$$

where h, k, l are the Miller indices. Combining (1) and (2),

$$\sin^2 \theta_{hkl} = \frac{\lambda^2}{4a^2} (h^2 + k^2 + l^2) = A(h^2 + k^2 + l^2) \tag{3}$$

References

1. R. W. M. D'Eye and E. Wait, *X-Ray Powder Photography in Inorganic Chemistry*, Butterworths, London, 1960.
2. N. F. M. Henry, H. Lipson and W. A. Wooster, *The Interpretation of X-Ray Diffraction Photographs*, Macmillan, London, 1960.
3. N. Booth, *Educ. in Chem.*, 1964, **1**, 66.
4. K. Lonsdale, *J. Chem. Educ.*, 1964, **41**, 240.

17.1 Investigation of a Powdered Solid Belonging to the Cubic System

You will be given a powder photograph of a compound which crystallizes in the cubic system. The objects of the experiment are: (i) to deduce whether the lattice is of the primitive (P), face-centred (F), or body-centred (I) type; (ii) to identify the compound by comparison of d-spacings with A.S.T.M. data from the file; and (iii) to deduce the cell dimension, a.

The worked example below refers to a film (figure 17.2) taken by

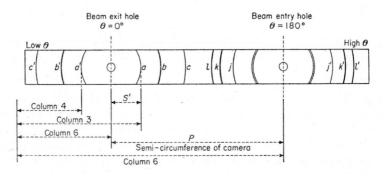

Figure 17.2. Powder photograph taken by the Straumanis method showing the measurements referred to in table 17.1.

the Straumanis method with copper K_α-radiation, using a commonly available powder camera (Philips' Debije-Scherrer, Type PW.1026). The double lines on the high-θ end of the film are due to resolution of the K_α-doublet [Cu($K_{\alpha 1}$) = 1·540 Å; Cu($K_{\alpha 2}$) = 1·544 Å] for the same reflection hkl. The dimensions of the camera are such that one degree of θ (the Bragg angle) corresponds to 1 mm. of the developed and stretched film.

Table 17.1

1	2	3	4	5	6	7	8	9	10
		Microscope readings cm.		Check	Undeflected beam readings			Corrected radii (R')	d Å
Line	Intensity	Left to right	Corresponding outer lines	$3 + 4$ = const. (± 0.1 mm.)		$3 - 6$ (R)	$6 - 4$ (R)		
a	10	11·10	5·47	16·57		2·814	2·818	2·770	3·227
b	5	12·32	4·24	16·56	Average/2 = 8·290	4·026	4·054	3·970	2·270
c	8	13·29	3·30	16·59		4·996	4·994	4·920	1·853
d	5	14·11	2·47	16·58		5·816	5·824	5·720	1·612
e	6	14·87	1·71	16·58		6·581	6·584	6·475	1·438
f	1	15·59	1·00	16·59		7·296	7·294	7·170	1·315
g	7	16·27	0·32	16·59		7·981	7·974	7·840	1·219
h	½	16·94	—	—		8·646	—	8·500	1·142

Procedure

(a) Mount the film below a travelling microscope with the low-θ lines on the left. List and record the line positions and intensities as in table 17.1. Count the strongest line as intensity 10 and grade other lines with reference to this. A weak line would have intensity 1 and a very weak line intensity $\frac{1}{2}$.

In table 17.1, only the low-θ lines are listed. A corresponding set of high-θ lines leads to the second undeflected beam position (i.e., the entry hole) as being at 265·93 mm. Thus, the semi-circumference of the camera, P, as measured from the film is $265·93 - 82·90 = 183·03$ mm. The true value of P is 180·00 mm.

The radii of the powder rings, R, must be corrected accordingly. The corrected values, $R = 2\theta$, in degrees, are in column 9. From tables, or from equation (1), calculate the d-spacings (column 10). Compare with the A.S.T.M. cards provided and thereby identify the compound. (Our example is caesium iodide.)

(b) Since the compound is known to be of cubic symmetry, it is simple to index the powder photograph and calculate the cell dimensions. Using the values of 2θ in table 17.1, compute $\sin^2 \theta$ (table 17.2). Then, by simple division, find the ratios of the $\sin^2 \theta$ values and compare them with table 17.3, which lists the permissible ratios for the cubic class. Note that seven is a forbidden number, and that in our example this number appears in table 17.2. The ratios are therefore doubled and it is seen that the numbers seven and fifteen do not now appear. The crystal is therefore of the body-centred cubic type. Assign indices and check that they correspond with the reflections on the A.S.T.M. card.

(c) Calculate a from the data in the tables and equation (3).

Table 17.2. Indexing

Line	$\sin^2 \theta$	Ratio	Ratio $\times$ 2	$h^2 + k^2 + l^2$	hkl
a	0·0571	1·000	2·000	2	110
b	0·1152	2·019	4·038	4	200
c	0·1733	3·037	6·074	6	211
d	0·2292	4·016	8·032	8	220
e	0·2867	5·024	10·048	10	310
f	0·3489	6·113	12·226	12	222
g	0·3994	6·998	13·996	14	321
h	0·4564	7·997	15·994	16	400

Table 17.3. Values of $(h^2 + k^2 + l^2)$ for the cubic system

Forbidden nos.	Primitive cubic P	Face-centred cubic F	Body-centred cubic I
	1		
	2		2
	3	3	
	4	4	4
	5		
	6		6
7			
	8	8	8
	9		
	10		10
	11	11	
	12	12	12
	13		
	14		14
15			
	16	16	16
	17		
	18		18
	19	19	
	20	20	20
	21		
	22		22
23			
	24	24	24
	25		

Chapter 18

Electrical Conductivity

Measurement of the electrical conductivity of an inorganic compound in solution gives a simple but valuable piece of structural evidence. Apart from the obvious question as to whether or not a given compound is an electrolyte, in a related series of compounds it may also be possible to determine how many ions per mole it contains. The most common solvents for this purpose are water ($\varepsilon = 81$), nitrobenzene ($\varepsilon = 35$) and nitromethane ($\varepsilon = 37$).

18.1 Electrical Conductivity of Solutions of Werner Complexes

Measure the electrical conductivity of a 0·001 M aqueous solution of each of the following:
  (i) $[Co(NH_3)_6]Cl_3$
  (ii) $[CoCl(NH_3)_5]Cl_2$
  (iii) $[Co(CO_3)(NH_3)_4]NO_3$
  (iv) $[Co(NO_2)_3(NH_3)_3]$
Rinse the conductivity cell with solution several times before making a measurement. Calculate the molar conductance from the cell constant, determined by measuring the electrical conductivity of an exactly 0·1 M aqueous solution of potassium chloride (Λ for 0·1 M K at 25°C is 128·96 ohm^{-1} cm.$^{-2}$). With (iv), take particular care to prepare a sample free from ionic impurities. Relate the observed conductivities of the solutions of (i)–(iv) to the number of ions per mole of complex. Consult manufacturers' instructions for operation of the conductivity bridge.

Exercises

1. Determine ionic chloride in complexes (i) and (ii). Determine total chloride in (ii) after decomposition with alkali, followed by acidification with sulphuric acid.

2. Draw out the stereochemical forms of each complex and suggest methods of differentiating between any isomers possible.

Preparation of complexes

Use stock samples if available. Only small quantities are needed for the experiment so that one preparation will probably provide enough material for the whole class. The object of the experiment is to study the conductivities of the complexes, not their preparation.

(i) *Hexa-amminecobalt(III) chloride, [Co(NH₃)₆]Cl₃.** Dissolve 12 g. ammonium chloride and 18 g. cobaltous chloride, $CoCl_2 \cdot 6 H_2O$, in 25 ml. boiling water. Add 1 g. decolourizing charcoal and cool in ice. Add 40 ml. concentrated ammonium hydroxide (0·880) and keep the solution at 10°c or lower. Add slowly, in small portions, 35 ml. ' 20 volume' hydrogen peroxide, briskly shaking the solution during the addition. Gradually raise the temperature to 50–60°c and keep the flask at this temperature, with frequent shaking, until the last trace of pink colouration is removed. Cool and filter. Tranfer the crystals to a beaker containing a boiling solution of 5 ml. concentrated hydrochloric acid in 150 ml. water. When all the solid, except the charcoal, has dissolved, filter the liquid while still hot. Add 20 ml. concentrated hydrochloric acid to the filtrate and cool the solution in ice. Collect the golden-brown crystals and dry them by washing with acetone. If necessary the complex may be recrystallized from water containing a trace of hydrochloric acid.

(ii) *Chloropenta-amminecobalt(III) chloride, [CoCl(NH₃)₅]Cl₂.* This preparation is given in experiment 6.1.

(iii) *Carbonatotetra-amminecobalt(III) nitrate, [Co(CO₃)(NH₃)₄] NO₃.* Add a solution of 20 g. ammonium carbonate in 100 ml. water and 50 ml. 0·880 ammonia to 10 g. cobalt nitrate in 20 ml. water. Draw a rapid stream of air through the mixture for three or four hours during which time the solution will change from deep blue to red. Concentrate the solution rapidly to 60 ml., maintaining an excess of ammonium carbonate by adding 1 g. every 15 min. – approximately 6 g. in all. Filter and concentrate to about 40 ml., adding a further 2 g. ammonium carbonate. Set the solution aside to crystallize. Collect the carmine crystals on a Buchner filter. Wash with a small quantity of cold water, then with alcohol. Dry in air. A further crop of crystals can be obtained by further evaporation of the mother liquor.

Reference

A. King, *Inorganic Preparations*, Allen and Unwin, Ltd., London, 1950, p. 110.

* Adapted from Palmer, *Experimental Inorganic Chemistry*.

(iv) *Trinitrotriamminecobalt*(III), $[Co(NO_2)_3(NH_3)_3]$. Suspend 3.5 g. (technical) cobalt carbonate in about 25 ml. hot water and dissolve the carbonate by addition of 8–10 ml. concentrated hydrochloric acid in portions. Filter the hot solution into a solution of 7·5 g. potassium bicarbonate in warm water. Boil the liquid now containing re-precipitated cobalt carbonate for 10 min. Filter the carbonate using a rather large filter funnel and wash it with hot water. Finally, dissolve the carbonate into the (emptied) filter flask with a hot mixture of 20 ml. water and 5 ml. glacial acetic acid.

Add the cooled solution of cobaltous acetate to a solution of 7·5 g. sodium nitrite in 35 ml. 0·880 ammonia. Cool the mixture in the ice-bath and, at 10°c or below, add slowly while mixing by vigorous shaking, 10 ml. ' 20 volume ' hydrogen peroxide. Keep the mixture in an ice-bath for 20 min. Then transfer the deep-brown liquid to a beaker and mark the level of the liquid on it. Add 7·5 g. ammonium carbonate and 0·5 g. decolourizing charcoal and heat – *in a fume cupboard* as much ammonia escapes. The liquid will soon become yellow and after 30–45 min. a yellow solid will begin to separate. The colour of the liquid is obscured by the charcoal but may be observed by swirling a thin layer around the beaker. During heating the volume of the contents of the beaker should be maintained undiminished.

When the separation of yellow solid indicates that reaction is complete, cool the beaker and its contents in ice and filter. Wash the crude solid with ice-cold water and then with ethanol. Remove the charcoal as follows: Take a volume of water equal in millilitres to thirty times the weight of the air-dried product in grams. Acidify with a few drops of acetic acid and boil. Add and dissolve the crude complex, filter while hot and set the filtrate aside for recrystallization. Wash the solid *very thoroughly* with cold water after collecting on a filter and dry at room temperature. Record the yield.

Reference

R. Duval, *Compt. Rend.*, 1938, **206**, 1652.

Chapter 19

Optical Isomerism in Inorganic Complexes

When optical isomerism occurs in inorganic complexes, the separation
of enantiomorphs is usually carried out by fractional crystallization
of a salt using an optically active organic anion or cation. Clearly, this
is only possible if the isomers are kinetically stable and do not
rearrange rapidly. A method of calculating the number of isomers
(optical and geometrical) possible for any complex with a specified
number of ligands, $M(X_l Y_m Z_n ...)$, has recently been published
(*Inorg. Chem.*, 1964, **3**, 265).

19.1 Preparation and Resolution of
Tris(ethylenediamine)cobalt(III) Chloride d-Tartrate

(i) $\qquad$ $CoSO_4 + en + HCl \xrightarrow{[0]} [Co(en)_3]SO_4 \cdot Cl$

(ii) $\qquad$ $[Co(en)_3]SO_4 \cdot Cl + Ba\ d\text{-tartrate} \rightarrow$

$\qquad$ $(+)$ and $(-)$-$[Co(en)_3]Cl \cdot d\text{-tartrate} \cdot 5\ H_2O + BaSO_4$

(iii) $\qquad$ $[Co(en)_3]Cl \cdot d\text{-tartrate} + NaI \rightarrow [Co(en)_3]I_3 \cdot H_2O$

$\qquad\qquad$ $+ Na_2\ d\text{-tartrate} + NaCl$

The sections (i)–(iii) below detail the procedure for the similarly
numbered reaction sequence above.

(i) Dissolve 11·5 ml. ethylenediamine (or the equivalent amount of
hydrate) in 25 ml. water in a filter flask. Cool the solution in ice and
add 10 ml. 10N hydrochloric acid, 14 g. cobalt sulphate, $CoSO_4 \cdot 7\ H_2O$,
dissolved in 25 ml. cold water, and 2 g. activated charcoal. Pass a rapid
stream of air through the solution for 4 hr. and then adjust the pH of
the solution to 7·0–7·5 using dilute hydrochloric acid or ethylenediamine. Heat the solution in an evaporating basin on a steam bath

163

for 15 min., cool, and filter off the charcoal. Wash the charcoal with 10 ml. water and add the washings to the filtrate which contains *tris(ethylenediamine)cobalt(III) chloride sulphate.*

(ii) To this solution add barium *d*-tartrate, which is prepared by mixing solutions of 12·2 g. barium chloride, $BaCl_2 \cdot 2H_2O$, and 7·5 g. *d*-tartaric acid at 90°C, cooling, filtering and washing with warm water. Heat the mixture on a steam bath with constant stirring for half an hour and then filter off the precipitated barium sulphate. Wash the precipitate with a little hot water and add the washings to the red filtrate, which is then evaporated to 30 ml. Allow to stand overnight, whereupon red crystals of (+)-*tris(ethylenediamine)-cobalt(III) chloride d-tartrate pentahydrate* form. Filter, and keep the filtrate which contains the (−)-*isomer.* Wash the crystals with aqueous ethanol and recrystallize from hot water (15 ml.) by cooling in ice. Wash the crystals with aqueous ethanol and then absolute ethanol. $[\alpha_D] = +102°$.

(iii) Dissolve the (+)-tris(ethylenediamine)cobalt(III) chloride *d*-tartrate in 15 ml. hot water and add 0·25 ml. concentrated ammonia solution followed, with stirring, by 17 g. sodium iodide in 7 ml. hot water. Cool in ice, filter and suck the crystals dry. Wash with ice-cold sodium iodide solution (3 g. in 10 ml.) to remove tartrate, and then with ethanol and acetone. The product is (+)-*tris(ethylenediamine)-cobalt(III) iodide monohydrate,* $[\alpha_D] = +89°$.

The (−)-*iodide isomer* is prepared as above from the filtrate* containing (−)-chloride *d*-tartrate. It should be recrystallized by dissolving in 40 ml. water at 50°C. Remove undissolved material, add 5 g. sodium iodide to the warmed filtrate and allow to crystallize. Filter, and wash the product with ethanol and acetone, $[\alpha_D] = -90°$.

Specific rotation, $[\alpha_D]$

Measure the specific rotation of your resolved salts.

Exercises

1. Why cannot $[Ni(en)_3]^{2+}$ be resolved?
2. Discuss the occurrence of optical isomerism in octahedral complexes containing monodentate ligands only.

Reference

J. A. Broomhead, F. P. Dwyer and J. W. Hogarth, *Inorg. Synth.*, **6**, 183.

APPENDICES

Appendix 1: Safety in the Laboratory

It is essential to adopt a positive approach to safety. No list of safety rules can cover all eventualities and, if there are a lot of rules, it is difficult to remember them. The design of each experiment, even if it be a simple test-tube reaction, should include a consideration of the hazards involved. Your attention is drawn particularly to the following points.

1. *Toxic chemicals*

The safest approach is to regard all chemicals other than water as toxic and to treat them as such, unless their safety is *definitely established*. Even some commonly used materials, e.g., benzene chromium trioxide, are highly dangerous. Throughout the text of this book there are many 'safety notes' relating to specific points, they are not necessarily comprehensive and, especially with advanced work (Section II), you should be particularly conscious of potential hazards.

If you are about to use a dangerous chemical (e.g., a cyanide) *first* of all find out how it may be *chemically deactivated*, and have the appropriate means to hand.

Disposal of dangerous residues and waste is not accomplished by simply pouring down the sink. Many laboratories have open traps and gases can easily find their way back into the laboratory air (e.g., cyanide residues, followed later by acids). Deactivate chemically before putting down a drain.

Mercury requires particular mention. It is a cumulative poison giving rise to very distressing physical and mental symptoms. Be extremely careful when handling it to avoid spillages. On the heated floors of modern laboratories, it will quickly vapourize. Recover any that is spilt with a suction device and dust the site liberally with flowers of sulphur.

> NOTE All vacuum lines containing mercury should be on a bench fitted with a raised continuous rim, so that spillages may be contained.

In order to give some indication of the relative toxicities of some of the compounds used in the experiments in this book, we have collected in the table below some 'threshold limit values'. 'They represent conditions under which it is believed that nearly all workers may be repeatedly exposed, day after day, without adverse effect'. These values should not be regarded as fine lines between safe and dangerous concentrations.

Threshold Limit Values (mg/cubic meter of air)
(Taken from *J. Occup. Medicine*, 1962, **4**, 545)

Acetone	2400	Hexane	1800
Acetonitrile	70	Hydrogen bromide	10
Ammonia	70	Hydrogen chloride	7
Benzene	80	Hydrogen cyanide – skin	11
Boron trifluoride	3	Hydrogen fluoride	2
Bromine	0·7	Hydrogen peroxide 90%	1·4
Carbon dioxide	9000	Hydrogen sulphide	30
Carbon disulphide – skin	60	Iodine	1
Carbon monoxide	110	Mercury	0·1
Carbon tetrachloride – skin	65	Methyl alcohol	260
Chlorine	3	Nickel carbonyl	0·007
Chlorobenzene	350	Nitric acid	25
Chloroform	240	Nitrobenzene – skin	5
Chromic acid and chromates	0·1	Nitrogen dioxide	9
1, 2-Dichloroethane	200	Osmium tetroxide	0.002
Dimethylformamide	60	Phosphine	0·07
Dimethylsulphate – skin	5	Phosphorus pentachloride	1
Dioxane	360	Phosphorus trichloride	3
Ethyl alcohol	1900	Sulphur dioxide	13
Ethylamine	45	Sulphur monochloride	6
Ethyl bromide	890	Tetrahydrofuran	590
Ethyl ether	1200	Toluene	750
Ethylenediamine	30	Trichloroethylene	520
Fluorine	0·2	Triethylamine	100
Formaldehyde	6	Xylene	870

2. *Fume cupboards*

Carry out all reactions involving dangerous and obnoxious volatile materials, either as starting materials or products, in a fume cupboard. This includes such operations as heating with concentrated acids, evaporations to dryness, etc.

A toxic vapour in a fume cupboard is still dangerous. Experiments should be so designed that dangerous gases or vapours given off during a reaction are trapped and chemically destroyed *before* they leave the apparatus contained in the fume cupboard. For example, it may be necessary to prepare dinitrogen tetroxide and pass it through a solution. Apparatus should be designed so that effluent gas from the solution is trapped out and chemically destroyed, *not* vented into a fume cupboard.

3. *Smoking*

Hazards created by smoking in the laboratory are (i) explosion in local concentrations of inflammable material, (ii) creation of toxic products by pyrolysis of vapours (chlorinated hydrocarbons are particularly dangerous as they will produce phosgene), and (iii) ingestion of toxic solids, etc., which may be picked up from a cigarette laid on a bench. For this reason, also, *it is best never to eat or drink in the laboratory.*

4. *Hazardous operations*

Hazards associated with the use of vacuum apparatus, liquid gases, high-pressure equipment, etc., are noted in the appropriate sections. Particular attention is drawn to the use of vacuum lines (pp. 78) and to the procedure for opening glass ampoules (Appendix 2).

Vacuum desiccators are potentially lethal (as anyone who has seen one implode will testify) and should never be evacuated unless fitted with a guard (supplied by the manufacturer). Do not store evacuated desiccators on the bench – put them in a cupboard.

5. *Safety equipment*

Safety glasses should be a standard item in every student's set of equipment. Rubber gloves are an optional extra, and should always be available. A supply of blast screens, desiccator guards, visors, etc., should also be available, and their use enforced when necessary.

6. *Overnight experiments*

These should be labelled with your name, the experiment involved, and instructions to an *unskilled person* who might have to take action to stop the experiment (e.g., nearest switch). It is best to leave overnight experiments in a fire-proof room if available. Check that *water connections* are securely clamped on, in case pressure rises. A fall in water pressure can also be dangerous: simple pressure operated switches are available which can be used to (say) turn off electrical equipment.

Appendix 2: Glass Techniques

The following brief descriptions deal with operations required in experiments described in the text. Further instruction can be obtained from the many excellent books available on glassworking techniques (see references).

Opening glass ampoules containing volatile liquids

Obnoxious and dangerous liquids and chemicals having a boiling point close to room temperature are supplied in sealed glass ampoules varying from 25 to 500 ml. Before opening, the ampoule must be cooled in an ice–salt mixture, or another cold bath (see Appendix 4) to reduce its vapour pressure. The cooling must be carried out *very carefully*: the ampoules are generally of soda glass and often have walls of uneven thickness. The entire opening operation must be carried out *in a fume cupboard*.

When cold, make a clean scratch about two-thirds of the way around the upper neck of the ampoule, using a good glass knife (NOT a file). Moisten the glass along the mark. While still cold, or immersed in the cold bath, break the neck of the ampoule at the scratch mark by the technique of 'hot-spotting' (see figure A2.1). Heat the end of

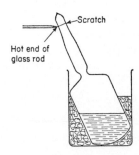

Figure A2.1. Opening a large ampoule by the technique of 'hot-spotting'.

170

a drawn-out piece of thin Pyrex glass rod (in a gas–oxygen flame) until red hot and press it firmly on the scratch. Thermal shock will cause a crack to spread around the mark and the end will probably fall off: knock it off otherwise.

Opening small-sample ampoules

Make a clean scratch about two-thirds of the way around the neck of the ampoule near the upper end. Use a good glass knife. Moisten the scratch and crack off the neck by the method of 'hot-spotting' described above.

NOTE   Do not open new (unused) ampoules by implosion in a flame: this leaves a shower of small glass fragments inside the ampoule.

Sealing small sample ampoules

Use a small, hot flame from a glass-blowing torch for this operation. Hold the bottom of the ampoule in one hand and while rotating it, heat the upper end of the open neck. When the glass softens, slowly pull the open neck away with a glass rod until the neck of the

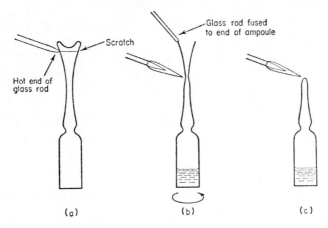

Figure A2.2. Opening and sealing small sample ampoules. (a) Opening a new ampoule by 'hot-spotting'. (b) and (c) Sealing an ampoule filled with liquid.

ampoule collapses and is sealed (figure A2.2). Finally, round off the sealed tip of the ampoule but do not heat for too long or the pressure of air inside will burst the top.

Sealing and opening Carius tubes

Carius tubes are made from heavy-walled Pyrex glass so that they will withstand high pressures of gases inside them. The technique for opening and sealing is similar to that described for ampoules but with the following differences (see figure A2.3).

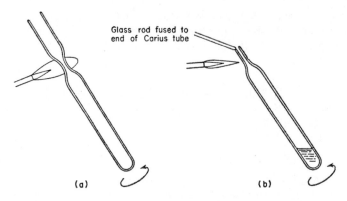

Figure A2.3. Preparing and sealing a Carius tube. (a) Pulling out the tube to make a neck through which the sample is admitted. (b) Sealing the neck of the Carius tube.

1. A hotter (gas–oxygen) and larger flame will be required because of the thicker glass.

2. When sealing, the heated area must be annealed to remove strains in the glass. This is carried out by evenly heating the whole neck area with a 'soft' flame, gradually lowering the temperature over a period of several minutes.

3. When opening a tube which may be pressurized, cool first, wrap the tube in cloth and protect your hands and eyes.

References

1. E. L. Wheeler, *Scientific Glassblowing*, Interscience, New York, 1958.
2. J. D. H. Heldmann, *Technique of Glass Manipulation in Scientific Research*, Prentice-Hall, New York, 1946.

Appendix 3: Purification of Solvents

Moisture-free solvents are essential in a number of reactions where the product, or intermediates, are water-sensitive. The method of removal of moisture is dependent upon the degree of purity required. The methods described below produce a solvent sufficiently dry for the preparations described in this book.

1. *Ether*
Leave the solvent in contact with sodium wire for 24 hr. If the sodium wire is found to be badly corroded, remove and repeat the treatment with fresh sodium.

2. *Benzene*
If the solvent is thought to be very wet, add calcium chloride and leave for 24 hr., with occasional shaking. Filter and then treat with sodium wire as for ether. Otherwise, treat directly with sodium wire.

3. *Pyridine*
Redistil followed by either
(a) leave the solvent in contact with sodium wire for 24 hr, as for ether, *or*
(b) reflux over sodium hydroxide pellets and then distil, rejecting the first and last fractions.

4. *Tetrahydrofuran (T.H.F.)*
Distil several times from fresh phosphorus pentoxide (100–200 g. per litre of solvent) until the solvent no longer significantly darkens a fresh batch of desiccant. At this stage, the T.H.F. may be stored for a few weeks *only* over sodium wire. *Immediately before use*, distil from lithium aluminium hydride (1 g. to 1 litre of solvent) to remove peroxides and traces of moisture.

Appendix 4: Cold Baths

The following cold baths are convenient for maintaining apparatus, etc., at low temperatures.

Ice–water	0°c
Ice–sodium chloride solution	0 to −22°c
* Liquid nitrogen–carbon tetrachloride	−23°c
* Liquid nitrogen–chloroform	−63°c
Solid carbon dioxide–acetone	−78°c
* Liquid nitrogen–carbon disulphide	−116°c
† Liquid nitrogen	−196°c

* These baths are prepared by slowly adding liquid nitrogen to the stirred liquid in a Dewar flask until a syrupy consistency is obtained. Do not allow a solid crust to form.

† When using liquid nitrogen take care to avoid condensation of liquid oxygen from the atmosphere in your apparatus.

Appendix 5: Desiccants and the Drying of Gases

For use in desiccators, the best desiccants are phosphorus pentoxide and Molecular Sieves (particularly convenient). Their value lies in their ability to produce very low humidities (dew points of about $-80°c$). Less effective desiccants are silica gel, activated alumina, concentrated sulphuric acid and potassium hydroxide pellets.

Low-boiling non-polar gases, e.g., nitrogen, oxygen, hydrogen, argon and the rare gases, are best and most efficiently dried by passing through a column (3 ft. $\times$ 1 in. diameter) containing Molecular Sieves (type 4A, 5A or 13X, $\frac{1}{8}$ in. or $\frac{1}{16}$ in. pellets). Molecular Sieves are *unsuitable* for drying carbon dioxide, hydrogen sulphide, sulphur dioxide, ammonia, chlorine, acetylene and ethylene.

Molecular Sieves are regenerated by pumping at $<10^{-2}$ mm. mercury for 24 hr. at 350°c.

Appendix 6: Literature

The following books and publications are valuable sources of information on preparative inorganic chemistry.

1. *Inorganic Syntheses*, Vol. 1, etc., McGraw-Hill.
2. G. Brauer, *Handbuch der Praparativen Anorganischen Chemie*, Ferdinand Enke, Stuttgart, 1954.
3. G. Brauer (Ed.), *Handbook of Preparative Inorganic Chemistry*, 2nd edition, Vols. I and II, Academic Press, New York, 1963.
4. R. E. Dodd and P. L. Robinson, *Experimental Inorganic Chemistry*, Elsevier, London, 1957.
5. W. G. Palmer, *Experimental Inorganic Chemistry*, Cambridge University Press, 1954.
6. G. G. Schlessinger, *Inorganic Laboratory Preparations*, Chemical Publishing Co. Inc., New York, 1962.
7. H. F. Walton, *Inorganic Preparations*, Prentice-Hall, New York, 1948.

Formula Index of Compounds Prepared

177

General Index

(For compounds prepared, see formula index)

179

LOGARITHMS

	0	1	2	3	4	5	6	7	8	9	1	2	3	4	5	6	7	8	9
10	·0000	0043	0086	0128	0170	0212	0253	0294	0334	0374	4	8	12	17	21	25	29	33	37
11	·0414	0453	0492	0531	0569	0607	0645	0682	0719	0755	4	8	11	15	19	23	26	30	34
12	·0792	0828	0864	0899	0934	0969	1004	1038	1072	1100	3	7	10	14	17	21	24	28	31
13	·1139	1173	1206	1239	1271	1303	1335	1367	1399	1430	3	6	10	13	16	19	23	26	29
14	·1461	1492	1523	1553	1584	1614	1644	1673	1703	1732	3	6	9	12	15	18	21	24	27
15	·1761	1790	1818	1847	1875	1903	1931	1959	1987	2014	3	6	8	11	14	17	20	22	25
16	·2041	2068	2095	2122	2148	2175	2201	2227	2253	2279	3	5	8	11	13	16	18	21	24
17	·2304	2330	2355	2380	2405	2430	2455	2480	2504	2529	2	5	7	10	12	15	17	20	22
18	·2553	2577	2601	2625	2648	2672	2695	2718	2742	2765	2	5	7	9	12	14	16	19	21
19	·2788	2810	2833	2856	2878	2900	2923	2945	2967	2989	2	4	7	9	11	13	16	18	20
20	·3010	3032	3054	3075	3096	3118	3139	3160	3181	3201	2	4	6	8	11	13	15	17	19
21	·3222	3243	3263	3284	3304	3324	3345	3365	3385	3404	2	4	6	8	10	12	14	16	18
22	·3424	3444	3464	3483	3502	3522	3541	3560	3579	3598	2	4	6	8	10	12	14	15	17
23	·3617	3636	3655	3674	3692	3711	3729	3747	3766	3784	2	4	6	7	9	11	13	15	17
24	·3802	3820	3838	3856	3874	3892	3909	3927	3945	3962	2	4	5	7	9	11	12	14	16
25	·3979	3997	4014	4031	4048	4065	4082	4099	4116	4133	2	3	5	7	9	10	12	14	15
26	·4150	4166	4183	4200	4216	4232	4249	4265	4281	4298	2	3	5	7	8	10	11	13	15
27	·4314	4330	4346	4362	4378	4393	4409	4425	4440	4456	2	3	5	6	8	9	11	13	14
28	·4472	4487	4502	4518	4533	4548	4564	4579	4594	4609	2	3	5	6	8	9	11	12	14
29	·4624	4639	4654	4669	4683	4698	4713	4728	4742	4757	1	3	4	6	7	9	10	12	13
30	·4771	4786	4800	4814	4829	4843	4857	4871	4886	4900	1	3	4	6	7	9	10	11	13
31	·4914	4928	4942	4955	4969	4983	4997	5011	5024	5038	1	3	4	6	7	8	10	11	12
32	·5051	5065	5079	5092	5105	5119	5132	5145	5159	5172	1	3	4	5	7	8	9	11	12
33	·5185	5198	5211	5224	5237	5250	5263	5276	5289	5302	1	3	4	5	6	8	9	10	12
34	·5315	5328	5340	5353	5366	5378	5391	5403	5416	5428	1	3	4	5	6	8	9	10	11
35	·5441	5453	5465	5478	5490	5502	5514	5527	5539	5551	1	2	4	5	6	7	9	10	11
36	·5563	5575	5587	5599	5611	5623	5635	5647	5658	5670	1	2	4	5	6	7	8	10	11
37	·5682	5694	5705	5717	5729	5740	5752	5763	5775	5786	1	2	3	5	6	7	8	9	10
38	·5798	5809	5821	5832	5843	5855	5866	5877	5888	5899	1	2	3	5	6	7	8	9	10
39	·5911	5922	5933	5944	5955	5966	5977	5988	5999	6010	1	2	3	4	5	7	8	9	10
40	·6021	6031	6042	6053	6064	6075	6085	6096	6107	6117	1	2	3	4	5	6	8	9	10
41	·6128	6138	6149	6160	6170	6180	6191	6201	6212	6222	1	2	3	4	5	6	7	8	9
42	·6232	6243	6253	6263	6274	6284	6294	6304	6314	6325	1	2	3	4	5	6	7	8	9
43	·6335	6345	6355	6365	6375	6385	6395	6405	6415	6425	1	2	3	4	5	6	7	8	9
44	·6435	6444	6454	6464	6474	6484	6493	6503	6513	6522	1	2	3	4	5	6	7	8	9
45	·6532	6542	6551	6561	6571	6580	6590	6599	6609	6618	1	2	3	4	5	6	7	8	9
46	·6628	6637	6646	6656	6665	6675	6684	6693	6702	6712	1	2	3	4	5	6	7	7	8
47	·6721	6730	6739	6749	6758	6767	6776	6785	6794	6803	1	2	3	4	5	5	6	7	8
48	·6812	6821	6830	6839	6848	6857	6866	6875	6884	6893	1	2	3	4	4	5	6	7	8
49	·6902	6911	6920	6928	6937	6946	6955	6964	6972	6981	1	2	3	4	4	5	6	7	8
50	·6990	6998	7007	7016	7024	7033	7042	7050	7059	7067	1	2	3	3	4	5	6	7	8
51	·7076	7084	7093	7101	7110	7118	7126	7135	7143	7152	1	2	3	3	4	5	6	7	8
52	·7160	7168	7177	7185	7193	7202	7210	7218	7226	7235	1	2	2	3	4	5	6	7	7
53	·7243	7251	7259	7267	7275	7284	7292	7300	7308	7316	1	2	2	3	4	5	6	6	7
54	·7324	7332	7340	7348	7356	7364	7372	7380	7388	7396	1	2	2	3	4	5	6	6	7
	0	1	2	3	4	5	6	7	8	9	1	2	3	4	5	6	7	8	9